The Open University

Energy and Light

Prepared by Sally Jordan

This publication forms part of an Open University course S104 *Exploring science*. The complete list of texts which make up this course can be found on the back cover. Details of this and other Open University courses can be obtained from the Student Registration and Enquiry Service, The Open University, PO Box 197, Milton Keynes MK7 6BJ, United Kingdom: tel. +44 (0)845 300 60 90, email general-enquiries@open.ac.uk

Alternatively, you may visit the Open University website at http://www.open.ac.uk where you can learn more about the wide range of courses and packs offered at all levels by The Open University.

To purchase a selection of Open University course materials visit http://www.ouw.co.uk, or contact Open University Worldwide, Michael Young Building, Walton Hall, Milton Keynes MK7 6AA, United Kingdom for a brochure tel. +44 (0)1908 858793; fax +44 (0)1908 858787; email ouw-customer-services@open.ac.uk

The Open University
Walton Hall, Milton Keynes
MK7 6AA

First published 2008

Edited and designed by The Open University.

Typeset by SR Nova Pvt. Ltd, Bangalore, India.

Printed in the United Kingdom by Halstan & Co. Ltd., Amersham, Bucks.

ISBN 978 1 8487 3164 6

2.1

Contents

Chapter 1
Introduction

The word 'energy' has been used extensively in the first two books of this course. Energy is required, for example, to drive the water cycle and to keep lithospheric plates in motion. However, energy is such an important concept that it warrants a more detailed investigation and that is the purpose of this book. Chapters 1–7 consider several different types of energy and the conversions between them. Chapters 8–11 turn specifically to energy coming from the Sun in the form of light and other radiation, which is important since the Sun is the energy source for almost all life on Earth (Figure 1.1).

Figure 1.1   Almost all life on Earth gets its energy from the Sun.

1.1   What is energy?

First, consider the everyday, non-scientific meaning of the word energy. If someone is described as being full of energy or very energetic, it conjures up a picture of a person who is very active, works hard, moves around quickly and probably accomplishes a lot. In science, the word energy is also associated with speed of movement, activity and work, but it is much more precisely defined and appears in many different guises. **Energy** is a physical property possessed by an object, and it is a measure of the capability of the object to 'make things happen'. In order for things to happen, some of the energy is usually transferred to another object.

One type of energy is inherent in the motion of an object, such as a football hurtling through the air. If the football hits a window and breaks it, then it is clear that the football's energy of motion has made things happen. This type of movement energy is called **kinetic energy** (from the Greek word *kinetikos*, meaning motion).

If you stay outside in the sun for too long and get sunburned, or use solar panels to provide hot water in your home, you will recognise that the energy carried in radiation from the Sun, usually called **solar energy**, also has the capability to make things happen.

■   Make a list of any other types of energy you can think of.

☐   Your list may include some of the following examples: nuclear energy, wind energy, wave energy, tidal energy, chemical energy, electrical energy, light energy (from sources other than the Sun), internal energy (expressed as the heat of an object), sound energy, energy from food (which can be considered a type of chemical energy), potential energy (including both gravitational potential energy and strain potential energy). Finally, you might be aware that mass, a quantity frequently associated with the amount of matter in an object, can also be considered a form of energy.

Einstein's famous equation $E = mc^2$ gives the relationship between energy E and mass m (c is the speed of light in a vacuum). Don't worry if this equation does not mean much to you at this stage, or if you have not thought about different forms of energy before. All of these aspects will be discussed thoroughly in this book. In doing this, Book 3 will use the mathematical tool of algebra. Don't panic! Algebra is simply a language; a very precise language that can describe mathematical ideas far more exactly and concisely than words can. Like all languages, it has its own rules and grammar which have to be learned and practised; that learning can be slow, but is nevertheless very rewarding. Even if you have had difficulty with mathematics before, please persevere. By the end of this book you will probably be astonished at your fluency in this new language.

The main skills focus of this book is the use of algebra, but you will also develop skills associated with problem solving, as well as further developing other skills that were introduced earlier in the course, particularly those associated with handling units and significant figures in calculations, and plotting and interpreting graphs. In addition, there are activities that develop the important practical work skills of measuring, recording and analysing data, and the communication skill of writing a report on an experiment you have done. The two experiments in this book, in Chapters 6 and 11, use only very simple equipment; objects that most people already have in their homes. These experiments nevertheless enable you to measure an important property of water and to gain a profound insight into the nature of light.

1.2   Planning your study of Book 3

You were encouraged to plan your study of Book 1 and Book 2 before starting to read them and you should do the same now for Book 3, by completing Activity 1.1. It is particularly important that you schedule the necessary time for the practical work in this book and make sure that you have access to all the equipment that you will need.

Activity 1.1   Planning your study of Book 3

We expect this activity will take you approximately 15 minutes.

As previously, the course Study Calendar provides a good starting point for planning your study. However, there are several specific aspects of Book 3 that are worth bearing in mind as you plan your studying for the next few weeks.

The mathematical nature of the subject matter means that the amount of time needed to complete the book will vary depending on how much maths you have done previously and how easy you found it. In particular, if you have not rearranged equations before, or if this has been a stumbling block for you in the past, you should allow extra time, especially for Chapters 3, 4 and 5. Don't be tempted to rush your reading of these chapters or to miss out the questions included for practice. Time spent understanding the rules of algebra will pay rich dividends throughout your study of this book, in later books of S104 and also if you continue your study of science.

There are two pieces of practical work in this book. The first one (in Activity 6.1, towards the end of Chapter 6) will take about an hour, although you will be taking measurements for only about 15 minutes. In this experiment you will be heating water in an electric kettle, so you may not be able to do the experiment in the place where you usually study; for example, you could not do it whilst travelling on a bus or train. The second piece of practical work in Activity 11.1 is the longest activity of this type in the whole course and, again, it would be difficult to do this experiment on the move. It will take you 2–3 hours to complete Activity 11.1 although you can choose to complete it in three separate parts, each of about 40 minutes – and you will only be taking measurements in the first two parts.

A timetable template, of the type you used in Books 1 and 2, is available in Activity 1.1 on the course website. You should use this grid to help you plan your study of Book 3, bearing in mind the points discussed above and any lessons learned from your study of Books 1 and 2.

In addition to planning when and where you will complete Activities 6.1 and 11.1, you should make sure that you already have access to or can obtain the necessary equipment. Activity 6.1 requires the use of an electric kettle and, preferably, a set of kitchen scales. Activity 11.1 needs two light bulbs, one of a tungsten filament type and one 'energy-saving' light bulb. The complete list of equipment required is given at the beginning of each activity and you are advised to check these lists now so that you have plenty of time to borrow or buy any of the household items that you don't already have access to. (The household items you will need are also listed in the *Course Guide*.)

There are no comments on this activity.

1.3   Summary of Chapter 1

Energy is a physical property possessed by an object, and is a measure of the capability of the object to 'make things happen'.

Kinetic energy is the energy that an object possesses by virtue of its motion.

The language of algebra can be used to express mathematical ideas in a precise and concise way.

In studying this chapter you have planned your study of Book 3, taking into account the mathematical nature of the book and its practical activities.

Chapter 2
Energy conversion and conservation

Energy can be transferred from one object to another. If you throw one of your S104 books up into the air (Figure 2.1), you transfer energy from the muscles in your arm to the book, and ultimately to the floor (assuming you do not catch the book). In this process, energy is also converted from one form into another. It starts as **chemical energy** stored in your body. Chemical reactions associated with muscle contraction release some of this energy, and it is converted into kinetic energy in your hand and in the book as it moves through the air. As the book rises it slows down, and so its kinetic energy decreases. However, the kinetic energy isn't destroyed; it is converted into a form of energy known as **gravitational potential energy**. This energy is discussed in detail in Chapter 5 and, similarly, other types of energy are discussed more fully in subsequent chapters. However, it is worth having a preliminary look at these forms of energy now, without worrying too much about the mathematical details which will come later. **Potential energy** is energy that is stored in some way, usually as a result of an object's position. Gravitational potential energy (sometimes simply referred to as gravitational energy) is the form of potential energy associated with gravity and it increases as an object moves further from the Earth's surface. Potential energy is so called because it has the potential to 'make things happen' at a later stage; the book's gravitational potential energy is converted back into kinetic energy as it falls. When the book strikes the floor a noise is produced (sound energy) and if you were to measure the temperature of the floor and the book after impact, with a *very* sensitive thermometer, you might record a slight increase in the temperature of both. An increase in the temperature of a substance is associated with an increase in the energy of its constituent molecules and the total energy of the constituent molecules of a substance is called its internal energy. This is discussed in more detail in Chapter 6.

Figure 2.1   Throwing a book in the air involves a variety of energy transfers and conversions.

Now consider the energy transfers and conversions that take place when a child jumps on a trampoline. When she is at the highest point of her bounce

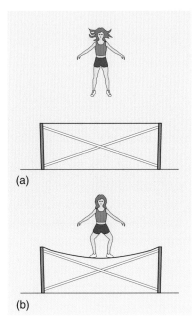

(a)

(b)

Figure 2.2   A child bouncing on a trampoline. (a) At the top of her bounce, gravitational potential energy is at a maximum. This is converted into kinetic energy as the girl falls. (b) As the trampoline distorts, energy is stored in the form of strain potential energy.

(Figure 2.2a), the girl's gravitational potential energy is at a maximum; as she falls back towards the trampoline, this decreases but, since she is moving faster and faster as she approaches the trampoline, her kinetic energy increases. When the girl hits the trampoline, her kinetic energy is converted into a different form of potential energy, this time **strain potential energy** in the trampoline as it distorts (Figure 2.2b). Strain potential energy is the energy stored within an object when it is stretched, squashed or otherwise deformed. In the case of the child on the trampoline, the strain potential energy is eventually returned to kinetic energy, enabling the girl to bounce into the air for a second time, gaining gravitational potential energy and losing kinetic energy as she gains height but loses speed. The process is then repeated.

As another example, consider the energy transfers and conversions involved in making a cup of tea using an electric kettle (Figure 2.3). Assume that the electricity is generated at a coal-fired power station. When the coal is burned, the chemical energy that was stored in it is converted into internal energy in steam, which is used to turn the turbine (kinetic energy) driving the generator that produces **electrical energy**. The electrical energy is supplied to your house and converted into internal energy of the kettle's heating element and then into internal energy of the water in the kettle, so the temperature of both increases. Some of this internal energy will be transferred to the kettle itself and to its surroundings, as well as to the tea cup and (eventually) yourself.

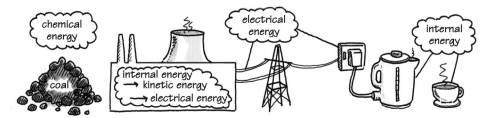

Figure 2.3   Energy transfers and conversions from chemical energy stored in coal to internal energy in a cup of tea.

In the examples described above, and in any other example you might think about, the law of **conservation of energy** applies. This means that the total amount of energy in all its different forms is always the same throughout any process, no matter what transfers or conversions take place. In the example of throwing a book up in the air, the book slows down as it rises and the decrease in its kinetic energy is balanced by the increase in its gravitational potential energy. The book speeds up as it falls and the increase in its kinetic energy matches the decrease in its gravitational potential energy, so that the total energy is always the same. Even after the book has come to rest on the floor, the increase in internal energy of the book and its surroundings (and any sound energy) will be exactly equal to the sum of the kinetic energy and the gravitational potential energy it had when it was thrown. In other words, energy is always conserved. This simple law appears to be true everywhere in the Universe and at all times, and can be summarised as follows.

The law of conservation of energy

Energy can be transformed from one form into another and transferred from one object to another, but it cannot be created or destroyed. In any process the total amount of energy is always constant.

The law of conservation of energy is extremely useful, but it is not always intuitively obvious.

■ Imagine that you are driving along a road. Since you are moving, your car (and you) will have a certain amount of kinetic energy; this has come from the chemical energy in the fuel you are using (or possibly from electrical energy). A small child runs out in front of you and you brake. You stop in time to avoid hurting the child, but where has the kinetic energy gone?

☐ Most of the energy is converted into internal energy, expressed as heat in the brakes of your car. In modern 'hybrid' cars, some of the kinetic energy is converted into electrical energy which is used to charge the battery. Some of the kinetic energy might also have been converted into sound energy, or in heating (or destroying) tyre rubber, as the car screeches to a halt. In popular speech, you might say that the car has 'lost' energy but, in reality, the energy has simply been transformed from one form to another one.

The law of conservation of energy was established by the British physicist James Prescott Joule in the 19th century. In order to do this, Joule had first to recognise that the different forms of energy are all fundamentally the same thing, something that had not been appreciated up to this time. The fact that different symbols are used for different types of energy (as you will discover in Chapters 3–7) is a reminder of the fact that scientists previously (and erroneously) considered, for example, heat and kinetic energy, to be completely different concepts. Joule worked in his father's brewery in Manchester, but he was so committed to his various scientific investigations that, after his marriage to Amelia Grimes in 1847, he is reputed to have spent several days of his honeymoon in the Alps investigating the energy transfers taking place in the Sallanches waterfall (La Cascade d'Arpenaz), shown in Figure 2.4. As the water falls, gravitational potential energy is converted into kinetic energy and sound energy. Joule reasoned that there should also be a conversion to internal energy at the base of the waterfall, so the water temperature should be slightly increased. He was right but, unfortunately, he did not have a sufficiently precise thermometer to enable him to detect the temperature increase. Joule's work on energy conservation and conversions has been recognised by the naming of the unit of energy, the joule, after him. Note that the name of the unit, joule, is conventionally written with a lower-case j, but its symbol J is always written with a capital letter (Book 1, Section 4.1).

Figure 2.4   Energy is converted from one form to others in waterfalls such as La Cascade d'Arpenaz.

Question 2.1

Describe the energy transfers and conversions that take place in the following situations:

(a) when a very bouncy rubber ball is dropped from about 1 metre above a solid surface and bounces repeatedly. (The height of each rebound will diminish until eventually the ball will stop bouncing. Why is this?)

(b) when electricity generated by wind turbines (Figure 2.5a) is used to power an electric light.

(c) when an archer shoots an arrow (Figure 2.5b) and the arrow flies through the air and hits a target 70 metres away.

(a)

(b)

Figure 2.5   Energy conversions take place (a) when electricity is generated by a wind turbine and (b) when an archer shoots an arrow.

c) muscle chemical energy → strain potential → Kinetic → Internal.

a) gravitational potential
Kinetic - moving
Internal - hits table Strain potential
Kinetic
Internal etc till stopped
with each bounce some energy is transferred from ball to surface (Sound + Heat)
So less energy in ball each time

b) Kinetic → electrical → Internal in filament → light energy

8

2.1 Summary of Chapter 2

Energy exists in several different forms. It can be converted from one form to another and transferred from one object to another.

The law of conservation of energy states that energy cannot be created or destroyed.

Potential energy is energy that is stored in some way, usually as a result of an object's position, with the potential to 'make things happen' at a later stage. Gravitational potential energy is associated with gravity and increases as an object moves farther from the Earth's surface. Strain potential energy is the energy stored within an object when it is stretched, squashed or otherwise deformed.

An increase in the temperature of a substance is associated with an increase in the energy of its constituent molecules; the total energy of the constituent molecules is referred to as the internal energy of the substance.

Energy can be stored as chemical energy and can be converted into electrical energy.

In studying this chapter you have used the law of conservation of energy to consider energy transfers and conversions in a qualitative way.

Chapter 3
Kinetic energy and algebra revisited

So far Book 3 has discussed energy transfers and conversions in a qualitative way but, in order to make measurements and do calculations, it is necessary to think quantitatively. The relationships between energy, in its various forms, and other quantities can best be expressed using algebra, where the word **algebra** describes the process of using symbols (usually letters) to represent quantities and the relationships between them. This chapter gives you an opportunity to review and consolidate some of the mathematical skills you have already learned and to develop new skills, in particular those associated with rearranging algebraic equations.

Activity 3.1   Reviewing some of the maths in Books 1 and 2

We expect this activity will take you approximately 15 minutes.

This activity gives you an opportunity to revise various mathematical skills that were developed earlier in the course.

(a) The equation $F = ma$ was introduced in Book 2, Section 14.2. Write down in words what this equation means. *force = mass × magnitude of acceleration.* ✓

(b) Which SI units should be used to measure each of the quantities F, m and a in the equation $F = ma$? *$F = N$ $kg\,ms^{-2}$ $M = kg$ $a = m\,s^{-2}$*

(c) In Book 1, Section 4.1, you learned that power is the amount of energy transferred per unit of time. (The concept of power is revisited in Chapter 4 of this book.) Write down a word equation for power in terms of energy transferred and time taken. Then choose symbols to represent each quantity involved and rewrite your equation using these symbols. *Power = energy transferred / time taken*

(d) A kettle transfers 3.4×10^5 J of energy in 2 minutes 15 seconds. What is its power? *2518 $J\,s^{-1}$* ✓ *$J = \frac{kW}{S}$ $P = \frac{J}{S}$*

Now look at the comments on this activity at the end of this book.

3.1   The equation for kinetic energy

Let's return to our study of energy and begin to think about the equation for kinetic energy. All moving objects have kinetic energy. Consider three such objects: a man walking along a road, an express train travelling across Europe and a bee flying through the air.

■ From your everyday knowledge, which of the three objects do you think will have the most kinetic energy and which will have the least?

□ The train will have the most kinetic energy, then the man walking along a road. The bee will have the least kinetic energy. There is no reason for you to be aware of the values of these energies at this stage, but you may like to know that the kinetic energy of the train is likely to be around 10^9 J, the kinetic energy of the man walking along the road will be around 50 J and the kinetic energy of the bee will be around 10^{-3} J.

■ These objects have widely different kinetic energies. The kinetic energy of any object depends on two properties. From your everyday experience of the world around you, what do you think these properties are?

☐ The kinetic energy of an object depends on its *mass* and its *speed*. In the above examples, the train has a very much larger mass than the man who in turn has a very much larger mass than the bee. The train also travels very much more quickly (most of the time). The man and the bee probably go at about the same speed.

Kinetic energy depends on both mass and speed, but speed has more of an effect than mass. You may have seen road safety campaigns emphasising the importance of driving slowly in built-up areas. This is because, whereas a doubling of the mass of your vehicle would result in a doubling in the kinetic energy, a doubling of speed (for example, from 50 kilometres per hour to 100 kilometres per hour) results in the kinetic energy of your car increasing by a factor of *four* (from around 1×10^5 J to around 4×10^5 J). If you were to reduce the speed of the car from 50 kilometres per hour to 5 kilometres per hour (that is, by a factor of ten), its kinetic energy would drop by a factor of a hundred (i.e. to approximately 1×10^3 J).

These findings are consistent with the fact that, using the symbols E_k for kinetic energy, m for mass and v for speed (i.e. magnitude of velocity), the kinetic energy of an object is given by the equation:

$$E_k = \tfrac{1}{2}mv^2 \qquad\qquad (3.1)$$

In words, kinetic energy is a half multiplied by mass multiplied by speed squared. Note that, since v^2 (said as v-squared, or v to the power two) means $v \times v$, speed is multiplied by itself in the equation for kinetic energy. This implies that, whereas if the object's mass is doubled then its kinetic energy will also be doubled, if the speed is doubled then the kinetic energy will be increased by a factor of four (since $2^2 = 4$). This is in line with the findings discussed above. If the mass is reduced by a factor of ten then the kinetic energy will be reduced by the same factor, but if the speed is reduced by a factor of ten, the kinetic energy will be reduced by a factor of a hundred (since $10^2 = 100$).

Now consider some of the other features of Equation 3.1:

• The symbol E refers to energy and the subscript k is used to make the meaning more specific. So E_k refers to kinetic energy. Note that although E_k uses two letters, it represents a single physical entity; E_k is not the same as Ek. When writing your own calculations you should make sure that this is clear.

• The '$\tfrac{1}{2}$' means that the kinetic energy is half of mv^2. Don't forget that multiplying by $\tfrac{1}{2}$ is equivalent to dividing by 2, so $E_k = \tfrac{1}{2}mv^2$ can also be written as $E_k = \dfrac{mv^2}{2}$.

• Only the v in the equation is squared, not the m. In the more general equation $a = bc^2$, the c should be squared but not the b. If you want the b to be squared as well, you should write b^2c^2 or $(bc)^2$.

3.2   The units of energy

Now consider a calculation whose result has already been quoted – the one to find the kinetic energy of a man walking along a road. Suppose he has a mass of 69 kg and walks at a speed of 1.2 m s^{-1}.

■ Substitute these values for m and v into Equation 3.1 to give a value for E_k.

☐ Using a calculator to find $\frac{1}{2} \times 69 \times (1.2)^2$ gives an answer of 49.68, which is 50 to two significant figures. However, this answer is incomplete without units. You know from Book 1 Section 4.1 that the SI unit of energy is the joule (symbol J), so the kinetic energy should be quoted as $E_k = 50$ J.

This answer is completely correct but you may be a little surprised that a value for mass is given in kg and a value for speed in m s^{-1}, yet the final answer for kinetic energy is given in J. What is the link?

The SI units of kg, m and s were introduced in Book 1, Box 2.1, and simple SI units such as these are known as **base units**. Since then you have encountered the SI units of m s^{-1} for speed, m s^{-2} for acceleration and kg m^{-3} for density. These units are all combinations of the base units m, kg and s. Some physical quantities are so commonly used that their units have names and symbols of their own, even though they could be stated as a combination of base units. You met the SI unit of force, the newton (N), in Book 2, Section 14.2 and you know that 1 N = 1 kg m s^{-2}.

Similarly, the joule can be expressed in base units as:

$$1 \text{ J} = 1 \text{ kg m}^2 \text{ s}^{-2} \tag{3.2}$$

■ Substitute the values given for the mass and energy of the man walking along a road in Equation 3.1 – complete with their units – and check for yourself that the units on the right-hand side of the equation work out as kg m^2 s^{-2}.

☐

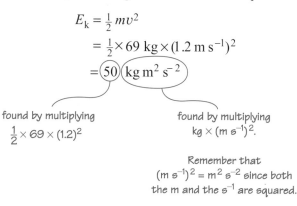

$$E_k = \tfrac{1}{2} mv^2$$
$$= \tfrac{1}{2} \times 69 \text{ kg} \times (1.2 \text{ m s}^{-1})^2$$
$$= \boxed{50} \; \boxed{\text{kg m}^2 \text{ s}^{-2}}$$

found by multiplying
$\frac{1}{2} \times 69 \times (1.2)^2$

found by multiplying
kg × (m s^{-1})^2.

Remember that
(m s^{-1})^2 = m^2 s^{-2} since both
the m and the s^{-1} are squared.

Note that, in order for the resulting units in any calculation of energy to be joules, the input values for mass and speed *must* be in SI units. So mass must be quoted in kg not g and speed must be in m s^{-1} not kilometres per hour (km h^{-1}) or miles per hour.

The link between a quantity and its units is a profound one. Had the units *not* turned out to be kg m^2 s^{-2} (i.e. joules) in this example, you would not have found an energy, and this would probably have indicated that a mistake had been made. You will be given further opportunities to practise your unit-handling skills throughout this book.

$$E_k = \tfrac{1}{2}mv^2$$

Question 3.1

Find the kinetic energy of:

(a) an athlete of mass 75 kg running at 8.5 m s^{-1}

(b) a lithospheric plate (Book 2, Section 8.1) of mass 4.0×10^{21} kg moving at 1.0×10^{-9} m s^{-1}.

[handwritten: $0.5 \times 75 \times 72.25$ $E_k = 520\,J \times$ $2760\,J$ or 2.7×10]

[handwritten: $2000\,J$]

[handwritten: 1×10^{-18}]

3.3 Rearranging equations

Suppose that, instead of knowing an object's mass, m, and speed, v, and wanting to find its kinetic energy, E_k, you know E_k and m and want to find v. The best way to proceed is to rearrange $E_k = \tfrac{1}{2}mv^2$ to make v the **subject** of the equation, where the word 'subject' is used to mean the term written by itself, usually on the left of the equals sign. Various equations were rearranged without explanation in Book 2 (e.g. $F = ma$ became $a = \dfrac{F}{m}$, and $s = \dfrac{d}{t}$ became $t = \dfrac{d}{s}$) and examples such as these are considered first before returning to the rather more complicated example of $E_k = \tfrac{1}{2}mv^2$. The general principles involved in rearranging equations remain the same, however complicated the equation may seem.

There are many different methods of rearranging equations and, if you are happy with a method you have learned previously, it is probably best to stick with it, provided it gives correct answers to the questions in this section. However, if you have not found a way of rearranging equations which you are comfortable with, you are advised to follow the method outlined here. This method draws on an analogy between an equation and an old-fashioned set of kitchen scales (Figure 3.1a), and considers the equation to be 'balanced' at the equals sign. The scales will remain balanced if you add a 50 g mass to one side of the scales, *provided* you do the same thing to the other side (Figure 3.1b). Similarly, the scales will remain balanced if the mass on *both* sides of the scales is halved (Figure 3.1c). In an analogous way, you can do (almost) anything you like to one side of an equation and, provided you do exactly the same to the other side, the equation is still valid.

The following rule summarises the discussion above.

> Whatever you do mathematically to one side of an equation you must also do to the other side.

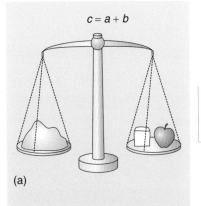

$c = a + b$

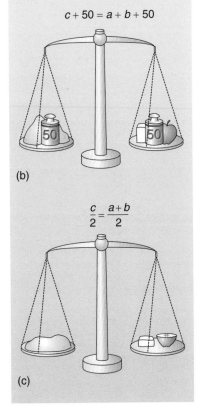

(a)

$c + 50 = a + b + 50$

(b)

$\dfrac{c}{2} = \dfrac{a+b}{2}$

(c)

Figure 3.1 (a) A set of kitchen scales. The scales remain balanced if (b) 50 g is added to both sides or if (c) the mass on both sides is halved.

This rule is fundamental when rearranging equations, but it doesn't tell you what operation to perform to both sides of an equation in order to rearrange it in the way you want. The highlighted hints on the following pages should help with this, as will plenty of practice. However, it is worth noting three points at the outset.

1 Even if you choose the 'wrong' operation, provided you correctly perform that operation to both sides of the equation, the equation will still be valid. Suppose you want to rearrange the equation $c = a + b$ to obtain an expression for a. You could divide by two, as illustrated in Figure 3.1c, which gives:

$$\frac{c}{2} = \frac{a+b}{2}$$

This is a perfectly valid equation; it just doesn't help much in your quest for a.

2 Equations are conventionally written with the subject on the left-hand side of the equals sign. However, when rearranging an equation it is often very helpful simply to reverse the order, so that the term on the left-hand side is moved to the right-hand side and vice versa.

So, if you derive or are given the equation $c = a + b$ you can rewrite it as $a + b = c$; if you derive or are given the equation $ab = c$ you can rewrite it as $c = ab$.

3 Addition and multiplication are **commutative**. This means that when two or more terms are added together, the addition can be done in any order, so

$$a + b = b + a$$

Similarly, when two or more terms are multiplied together, the multiplication can be done in any order, so

$$ab = ba$$

(Subtraction and division are not commutative, so the order in which subtractions and divisions are carried out makes a difference to the answer.)

You will also find it useful to remember that $a \times \dfrac{b}{c}$ is the same as $\dfrac{a \times b}{c}$ or $\dfrac{a}{c} \times b$.

If you have difficulty in understanding these examples when expressed in terms of the letters a, b and c, you may find it helpful to think in terms of numbers, such as 2, 3 and 4: so

$$2 + 3 = 3 + 2$$
$$2 \times 4 = 4 \times 2$$

and

$$2 \times \frac{3}{4} = \frac{2 \times 3}{4} = \frac{2}{4} \times 3$$

However, remember that these rules are true for all values of a, b and c.

Returning to the quest for a method for rearranging equations, the hints that follow provide additional helpful guidelines, and each hint is followed by an example of its use. Note that the words expression and term are used to describe the parts of an equation. An equation must always include an equals sign, but an expression or term won't.

Hint 1   If you want to remove an expression that is *added* to the term you want, *subtract* that expression from both sides of the equation.

To rearrange $a + b = c$ to make a the subject, note that you need to remove the b from the left-hand side of the equation. The b is currently added to a, so you need to subtract b from both sides. This gives:

$$a + b - b = c - b$$

or $a = c - b$ (since $b - b = 0$).

Hint 2   If you want to remove an expression that is *subtracted* from the term you want, *add* that expression to both sides of the equation.

To rearrange $a - b = c$ to make a the subject, note that you need to remove the b from the left-hand side of the equation. The b is currently subtracted from a, so you need to add b to both sides. This gives:

$$a - b + b = c + b$$

or $a = c + b$ (since $-b + b = 0$).

Hint 3   If the term you want is *multiplied* by another expression, *divide* both sides of the equation by that expression.

To rearrange $ab = c$ to make a the subject, note that you need to remove the b from the left-hand side of the equation. The a is currently multiplied by b, so you need to divide both sides of the equation by b. This gives:

$$\frac{ab}{b} = \frac{c}{b}$$

The b in the **numerator** (top line) of the fraction on the left-hand side cancels with the b in the **denominator** (bottom line) to give:

$$a = \frac{c}{b}$$

Hint 4   If the term you want is *divided* by another expression, *multiply* both sides of the equation by that expression.

To rearrange $\dfrac{a}{b} = c$ to make a the subject, note that you need to remove the b from the left-hand side of the equation. The a is currently divided by b, so you need to multiply both sides of the equation by b. This gives:

$\dfrac{a}{b} \times b = c \times b$, which can also be written as $\dfrac{a \times b}{b} = c \times b$

The b in the numerator of the fraction on the left-hand side cancels with the b in the denominator to give:

$a = c \times b$, which can be written as $a = cb$

Hints 1 to 4 all follow from a general principle:

To 'undo' an operation (e.g. $+$, $-$, $\times$, $\div$) you should do the opposite, (i.e. $-$, $+$, $\div$, $\times$).

The following worked examples should help you to see how to apply the basic rules.

Worked example 3.1

Rearrange $F = ma$ to make m the subject of the equation.

It is helpful to start by reversing the order of the equation, so that m is on the left-hand side. Thus $F = ma$ can be written as:

$$ma = F$$

To isolate m you need to remove a, and m is currently *multiplied* by a so, from Hint 3, you need to *divide* by a. Remember that you must do this to both sides of the equation, so you have:

$$\frac{ma}{a} = \frac{F}{a}$$

The a in the numerator (top line) of the fraction of the left-hand side cancels with the a in the denominator (bottom line) to give:

$$m = \frac{F}{a}$$

Worked example 3.2

Rearrange $\rho = \dfrac{m}{V}$ (the equation for density, ρ, introduced in Book 2, Section 11.2.1) to obtain an equation for m.

Reversing the equation gives:

$$\frac{m}{V} = \rho$$

Now, m is on the left-hand side but it is *divided* by V. To remove V from the left-hand side, you need to *multiply* both sides by V (Hint 4) to give:

$\dfrac{m}{V} \times V = \rho \times V$, which can also be written as $\dfrac{m \times V}{V} = \rho \times V$

The V in the numerator of the fraction of the left-hand side cancels with the V in the denominator to give:

$m = \rho \times V$, which can be written as $m = \rho V$

To check that you can apply Hints 1 to 4, try answering Question 3.2 now. The equations in this question are introduced later in this book, but you don't need to worry about their meaning yet.

Question 3.2

(a) Rearrange $v = f\lambda$ to make f the subject (λ is the Greek letter lambda). $f\lambda = v$　$\dfrac{f\lambda}{\lambda} = \dfrac{v}{\lambda}$　$f = \dfrac{v}{\lambda}$

(b) Rearrange $E_{tot} = E_k + E_g$ so that E_k is the subject. $E_{tot} = E_k + E_g$

$E_k^{+G} = E_g = E_{tot} - E_g$　$E_k = E_{tot} - E_g$

(c) Rearrange $I = \dfrac{Q}{t}$ to obtain an equation for Q.

$\dfrac{Q}{t} = I$　$\dfrac{Q}{t} \times t = I \times t$　$v = IL$

$\dfrac{Q}{t} = I$　$\dfrac{Q}{t} \times t = I \times t$　$t\rho$　$Q = I\rho$

The equation $E_k = \frac{1}{2}mv^2$ is slightly more complicated than the equations you rearranged in Question 3.2. This is partly because it includes a squared term, v^2.

■ What do you need to do in order to 'undo' a square?

☐ You need to find the square root (Book 2, Box 13.1).

Recall that $3^2 = 9$, $5^2 = 25$ and $10^2 = 100$. You can undo each square by saying that the square root of 9 is 3, that the square root of 25 is 5 and that the square root of 100 is 10. In symbols, $\sqrt{9} = 3$, $\sqrt{25} = 5$ and $\sqrt{100} = 10$. Strictly, this definition of square root is not complete; $3 \times 3 = 9$ but also $(-3) \times (-3) = 9$, so the square root of 9 could be either 3 or –3, and so on for other numbers. You should write $\sqrt{9} = \pm 3$, $\sqrt{25} = \pm 5$, $\sqrt{100} = \pm 10$, where '$\pm$' indicates that the answer could be either positive or negative (the $\pm$ notation was the same as you used when considering uncertainties in Book 1, Section 3.1.2). The negative square root can be very important, but the rest of this course uses only positive square roots, so the negative ones will be omitted for simplicity.

Make sure that you know how to use your calculator to find a square root. It probably has a key marked '$\sqrt{}$' but, if not, you may need to recall that square roots can also be expressed using fractional powers (Book 2, Box 13.1). So, $\sqrt{a}$ can be written as $a^{1/2}$ or $a^{0.5}$.

■ Use your calculator to find $\sqrt{3.61}$. $1 \cdot 9$

☐ Your calculator should give the answer as 1.9.

The rules for 'undoing' operations when rearranging equations can now be extended.

> Hint 5   If you are trying to make a term the subject of an equation and you currently have an equation for the *square* of that term, take the *square root* of both sides of the equation.

To rearrange $a^2 = b$ to make a the subject, note that a is currently squared, and so take the square root of both sides of the equation to give:

$$a = \sqrt{b}$$

> Hint 6   If you are trying to make a term the subject of an equation and you currently have an equation for the *square root* of that term, *square* both sides of the equation.

To rearrange $\sqrt{a} = b$ to make a the subject, note that you currently have an equation for the square root of a, and square both sides of the equation to give:

$$a = b^2$$

When rearranging more complicated equations, it is often helpful to proceed in several steps. Each step will use the rules already discussed, but many people are perplexed when trying to decide which step to take first. Expertise in this area comes largely with practice, and there are no hard-and-fast rules (often an equation can be arranged by several, equally correct routes). However, the following hints may help.

Hint 7 Don't be afraid of using several small steps to rearrange one equation.

Hint 8 Aim to get the new subject into position on the left-hand side as soon as you can. (This is not always possible straight away.)

Simply reversing an equation can be a useful way of getting the new subject into position on the left-hand side, but this is not always the case. Consider the equation $s = \dfrac{d}{t}$ and imagine that you want to express this equation in terms of t, i.e. to make t the subject. t is currently the term in the denominator of the fraction on the right-hand side of the equation. The way to get this term (by which d is *divided*) into position on the left-hand side is to *multiply* both sides by t:

$$s \times t = \frac{d \times t}{t}$$

Cancelling the t terms on the right-hand side gives:

$$s \times t = d$$

The t is now in place on the left-hand side of the equation, but you still need to remove the s. The t is currently *multiplied* by s, so you should *divide* both sides by s to give:

$$\frac{s \times t}{s} = \frac{d}{s}$$

i.e. $\quad t = \dfrac{d}{s}$

Hint 9 You can treat an expression within brackets as if it was a single term. This is true whether the brackets are shown explicitly in the original equation or whether you have added them (or imagined them) for clarity. If the quantity required as the subject is itself part of an expression in brackets in the original equation, it is often best to start by making the whole bracketed term the subject of the equation.

We can now return to Equation 3.1, $E_k = \frac{1}{2}mv^2$, and rearrange it to make v the subject. Remember that this equation can be written as $E_k = \dfrac{mv^2}{2}$. Let's imagine there are brackets around (v^2) and start by finding an expression for v^2 (see Hint 9). $E_k = \dfrac{mv^2}{2}$ can be reversed to give:

$$\frac{mv^2}{2} = E_k$$

which has v^2 on the left-hand side (Hint 8).

Now we can proceed in a series of steps (Hint 7).

To remove the 2 from the denominator on the left-hand side, multiply both sides by 2 (Hint 4):

$$2 \times \frac{mv^2}{2} = 2E_k$$

i.e. $mv^2 = 2E_k$

To remove the m, divide both sides by m (Hint 3):

$$\frac{mv^2}{m} = \frac{2E_k}{m}$$

The m terms on the left-hand side cancel to give:

$$v^2 = \frac{2E_k}{m}$$

Finally, taking the square root of both sides gives:

$$v = \sqrt{\frac{2E_k}{m}} \tag{3.3}$$

This equation for v cannot be simplified any further.

Note that the square root sign has been drawn so that it goes right around the $\frac{2E_k}{m}$. This means that the square root applies to the whole of $\frac{2E_k}{m}$; you may find it helpful to imagine (or even to draw) brackets around the term to indicate that the square root applies to all of it:

$$v = \sqrt{\left(\frac{2E_k}{m} \right)} \tag{3.4}$$

Since square roots can be expressed using fractional powers (Book 2, Box 13.1), Equation 3.4 could also have been written as

$$v = \left(\frac{2E_k}{m} \right)^{1/2}$$

You will see more examples of rearranging equations shortly. However, it is important not to lose sight of *why* we were rearranging Equation 3.1. We wanted to find an object's speed from given values of kinetic energy and mass.

■   Return to the example of the express train travelling across Europe. If a train of mass 3.9×10^5 kg has a kinetic energy of 9.8×10^8 J, how fast is it travelling?

☐   We can use Equation 3.3 (the rearranged form of Equation 3.1), and substitute the given values for E_k and m to find a value for v. In working out the units, it is helpful to remember that 1 J = 1 kg m² s⁻² (Equation 3.2).

$$v = \sqrt{\frac{2E_k}{m}}$$

$$= \sqrt{\frac{2 \times 9.8 \times 10^8 \text{ J}}{3.9 \times 10^5 \text{ kg}}}$$

$$= \sqrt{\frac{2 \times 9.8 \times 10^8 \text{ kg m}^2 \text{ s}^{-2}}{3.9 \times 10^5 \text{ kg}}}$$

$$= \sqrt{5025.641 \text{ m}^2 \text{ s}^{-2}}$$

$$= 71 \text{ m s}^{-1} \text{ to two significant figures}$$

Note that, in working out the units, the kg in the numerator of the fraction cancelled with the kg in the denominator. Also the last step involved finding the square root of both the number and its units. Since $(\text{m s}^{-1})^2 = \text{m}^2 \text{ s}^{-2}$ it follows that the square root of $\text{m}^2 \text{ s}^{-2}$ is m s^{-1}, i.e. $\sqrt{\text{m}^2 \text{ s}^{-2}} = \text{m s}^{-1}$.

This example is revisited in the video sequence *Working out the Units* in Activity 4.2.

3.4   Changes in kinetic energy

Imagine a skier on a downhill run. His speed will increase as he descends and there will be a corresponding increase in his kinetic energy.

■ Recall the law of conservation of energy from Chapter 2. What is the source of the skier's increase in kinetic energy?

☐ The law of conservation of energy states that energy can be transformed from one form into another but it cannot be created or destroyed. In this case a decrease in the skier's gravitational potential energy leads to the increase in kinetic energy. Some of the gravitational potential energy will be converted into other forms too, probably internal energy (heat) and sound energy.

There is a quantitative discussion of gravitational potential energy in Chapter 5. For now, we will just write an equation for the increase in kinetic energy. Using the symbol m to represent the skier's mass, u to represent his initial speed and v to represent his final speed, the skier's initial kinetic energy is $\frac{1}{2}mu^2$ and his final kinetic energy is $\frac{1}{2}mv^2$.

■ What is the increase in the skier's kinetic energy?

☐ The increase is the difference between the initial kinetic energy and the final kinetic energy, so we can write:

increase in kinetic energy = final kinetic energy − initial kinetic energy

$$= \frac{1}{2}mv^2 - \frac{1}{2}mu^2$$

or

$$\Delta E_k = \frac{1}{2}mv^2 - \frac{1}{2}mu^2 \qquad\qquad (3.5)$$

The Greek upper-case letter Δ (**delta**) is frequently used to represent the change in a quantity. Thus:

Δx means 'the change in x' and is said as 'delta-x'.

By convention, a positive value of Δx implies an increase in the quantity x while a negative value of Δx implies a decrease in the quantity x.

ΔE_k represents the change in kinetic energy. Note that the symbols Δ, E and the subscript k are used together to represent a single quantity, ΔE_k, and you should not attempt to separate the symbols when they are used in this way.

Since the $\frac{1}{2}$ and the m are the same in both terms on the right-hand side of Equation 3.5, it could be written as $\Delta E_k = \frac{1}{2}m(v^2 - u^2)$ since the brackets mean that both the v^2 and the u^2 must be multiplied by $\frac{1}{2}m$. However, note that the expression on the right-hand side of Equation 3.4 is *not* the same as $\frac{1}{2}m(v - u)^2$, which would imply that u should be subtracted from v and that value should be squared rather than squaring the v and the u separately before one is subtracted from the other. This point emphasises the importance of writing mathematical expressions very carefully. This becomes easier with practice.

The equation $\Delta E_k = \frac{1}{2}mv^2 - \frac{1}{2}mu^2$ is the most complicated one to be rearranged in Activity 3.2. There it simply serves as an example of how relatively complex equations can be rearranged by applying the same rules that are used when rearranging simple equations.

3.5   Practising what you have learned

Activity 3.2 is a video sequence in which a student and a tutor discuss the way in which various equations can be arranged using the guidelines given in this chapter. You should study this activity and then try Questions 3.3 and 3.4.

Activity 3.2   Rearranging equations

We expect this activity will take you approximately 45 minutes.

A number of hints have been introduced throughout this chapter to help you when rearranging algebraic equations. The video sequence *Rearranging Equations* illustrates the use of these hints in rearranging equations of increasing complexity. You will soon realise that the principles involved remain the same, no matter how complex the equation appears to be.

You should now watch the video sequence *Rearranging Equations*. You may find it helpful to view the video once without stopping and then replay it, pausing from time to time to check your understanding.

You will be encouraged to stop the sequence towards the end and to answer parts of Question 3.3 at that stage.

There are no comments on this activity.

Question 3.3

(a) Rearrange $E = mc^2$ to make c the subject.

(handwritten) $\dfrac{E}{m} = \dfrac{mc^2}{m} = \dfrac{E}{m} = c^2 \quad c = \sqrt{\dfrac{E}{m}}$

(b) Rearrange $\rho = \dfrac{m}{V}$ so that V is the subject.

(handwritten) $\rho \times V = \dfrac{m}{V} \times v = \rho V = m = V = \dfrac{m}{\rho}$

(c) Rearrange $a = \dfrac{v - u}{t}$ to obtain an equation for v.

(handwritten) $a = \dfrac{v - u}{t} \qquad at = v - u \qquad at + u = v$

Question 3.4

(a) Rearrange Equation 3.1, $E_k = \frac{1}{2}mv^2$, to make m the subject.

(handwritten) $\dfrac{mv^2}{2} = E_k \qquad 2E_k = mv^2$

(b) Use your answer to part (a) to find the mass of the bee described in Section 3.1, which has a speed of 4.5 m s^{-1} and a kinetic energy of 1.0×10^{-3} J.

(handwritten) 9.9×10^{-5} kg.

(handwritten) $\dfrac{0.002}{20.25}$

(handwritten) $m = \dfrac{2E_k}{v^2}$

3.6 Summary of Chapter 3

If an object with mass m is moving with speed v then its kinetic energy E_k, is given by $E_k = \frac{1}{2}mv^2$.

The SI unit of energy is the joule: 1 J = 1 kg m^2 s^{-2}.

In studying this chapter you have revised some of the mathematics introduced earlier in the course and you have applied a series of hints in order to rearrange equations.

Equations can be rearranged using the basic rules:

- whatever you do mathematically to one side of an equation you must also do to the other side
- to 'undo' an operation (e.g. +, −, ×, ÷, square, square root) you should do the opposite (i.e. −, +, ÷, ×, square root, square)
- complicated equations can be rearranged in a series of small steps.

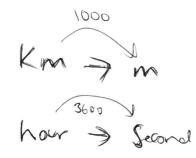

Chapter 4
Work, energy and power

The concept of power was introduced in Book 1, and the discussion of Newton's laws of motion in Book 2 depended on an understanding of the concept of force. This chapter introduces the scientific meaning of the word 'work' and describes how this relates to what you already know about energy, force and power.

In this chapter, and the ones that follow, you will meet several new equations involving a variety of symbols. Generally, scientists are careful to specify the meaning of the symbols that they use when writing books or scientific papers, and this is done in this course too. However, it is impractical to specify the meaning of a symbol every time it is used, and it would become extremely repetitive and boring if this was done. So you may sometimes meet a symbol whose meaning you are unsure of. You may also sometimes want to check up on the correct SI units for a quantity. Activity 4.1 will help you to keep track of important symbols, units and equations.

Activity 4.1   Keeping track of symbols, units and equations – Part 1

We expect this part of the activity will take you approximately 15 minutes.

To keep track of the symbols that are introduced and to help you remember their meanings, you should produce your own glossary of symbols and their meanings as you first meet them. You will also find it helpful to note down the appropriate SI unit for the quantity represented by the symbol, and the meaning of this unit in terms of base units. It is up to you to decide where to keep your glossary; you could perhaps use a notebook or a word-processed file in your study folder. It is also up to you to decide how your glossary entries should be arranged. One possibility is to arrange them in a table, for example:

Symbol	Meaning	Units	Base units
E_k	kinetic energy	J	$1 \text{ J} = 1 \text{ kg m}^2 \text{ s}^{-2}$

If you keep your glossary handy while studying this book, you can refer to it when you meet a symbol that you are unsure of, and won't have to hunt through the text to find where it was first defined. You could list the symbols conventionally used for mass, volume, density, speed, time, acceleration, force and kinetic energy now, and then add others as you progress through the course. You could also include mathematical notation in your glossary, for example the Δ symbol, which was introduced in Chapter 3 and means 'change in'.

When listing the meanings of symbols be particularly careful to look out for letters with more than one meaning (e.g. as you know from Book 1, Section 4.1, the letter W represents the watt, but you will soon discover that W represents work) and to use the appropriate case for each (so J must be written with a capital J, but kg, m and s are all written in lower case). If you are having difficulty in distinguishing between the symbols used to represent physical quantities and those used for units, remember that in printed text the letters used to represent physical quantities are printed in *italic* whereas those used for units are not. If you are word-processing your glossary you can follow the same convention.

At the same time as compiling a glossary of symbols and units, you will find it useful to list important equations as you meet them in. Alongside each equation you should write down the meaning of all of the symbols used and the appropriate SI unit for each. One way of doing this (using a familiar example from Chapter 3) is as follows.

Equation	Meaning of symbols (and units)
$E_k = \frac{1}{2}mv^2$	E_k is kinetic energy (J) m is mass (kg) v is speed (m s^{-1})

If you keep this list handy while you are studying the book, and refer to it when you are answering questions, you will soon become familiar with the equations.

The equations that are particularly important are displayed as key points in the course books and given in the chapter summaries. You will not be expected to remember these equations, but you will find it helpful if you can begin to recognise which equation it is appropriate to use in a particular situation, and the meaning of each term in the equation.

You should add the equations for density, speed, acceleration, force and kinetic energy to your list now.

There are no comments on this activity.

4.1   Force and work

The word work has a very specific meaning in science, but this is closely related to the way in which it is sometimes used in everyday life. You probably know that pushing a broken-down car along a road involves a lot of work – this is true according to both the everyday and the scientific meanings of the word.

In discussing the scientific definition of work, consider another everyday example: a child setting a toy train in motion along a track by giving it a push (Figure 4.1). To keep the example as simple as possible, you should make the following assumptions:

train initially stationary, no motor, no brakes, no friction

constant force applied by child

Figure 4.1 A child pushing a train to set it in motion along a very long, straight horizontal track.

- the train is initially stationary
- the train has no motor, so its motion depends entirely on the push given by the child
- the track is straight, horizontal and very long
- the train has no brakes and there is no friction anywhere within the moving parts of the train
- the rotational movement of the train's wheels can be ignored and you can simply consider the movement of the train as a whole
- the child provides a *constant* force for the length of time she is pushing the train.

Although some of these assumptions may seem unrealistic, they will prove to be very useful. It is often easier to grasp how things work by first thinking about the simplest possible situation. This kind of thought experiment has led to some very important scientific discoveries. Once you have a clear picture of the simple case, you can gradually add in complications (to make it more realistic) and see what effect they have.

4.1.1 What is work?

In Book 2, Chapter 14 you learned about Newton's laws of motion. You can apply that knowledge to the example of the toy train.

- ■ What is Newton's first law of motion?

- □ Newton's first law states that an object will continue moving at constant speed in a straight line (or remain at rest) unless acted upon by an unbalanced force.

- ■ If the train is set in motion with a certain speed along the horizontal track, how long will it keep moving at the same speed?

- □ If the train is truly frictionless and the track is horizontal, there is no unbalanced force acting on the train and it will continue moving at the same speed indefinitely (or at least, until it reaches the end of the track).

Before being pushed, the train is stationary and so has no kinetic energy. After the push, the train has a certain speed and hence a certain kinetic energy, and it seems reasonable to assume that the kinetic energy is provided by the push. It also seems reasonable to assume that the greater the strength of the push, the greater the quantity of energy that is transferred to the train, since the train certainly travels faster.

The energy transferred to an object by a force is an important quantity and is given a special name. It is called the **work** done by the force on the object. The greater the force that is applied, the greater the work that is done, and the greater the energy transferred to the object on which the force acts. However, the dependence of work on the force applied isn't the whole story. In a typically vigorous push, the child's hand might stay in contact with the train for, say, 20 cm. If she applied the same force but only stayed in contact with the train for 5 cm, the train would not reach such a high speed. So it seems that the energy transferred by the force also increases when the distance over which the force is applied increases.

4.1.2 Pondering proportionality

The work that is done by the force on an object turns out to be **directly proportional** to both the magnitude (size) of the force and the distance over which the force is applied.

In general, two quantities are said to be directly proportional (or simply proportional) to each other if, when the value of one is multiplied (or divided) by a certain amount, the value of the other also becomes multiplied (or divided) by the same amount. For example, the cost of petrol is proportional to the volume of petrol bought, so the cost of buying 50 litres of petrol is twice the cost of buying 25 litres which is five times the cost of buying 5 litres.

The symbol '∝' is used to mean 'is proportional to' so, for petrol, you can write:

total cost ∝ volume

Another way of writing this is:

$$\text{total cost} = \text{constant} \times \text{volume}$$

The constant is known as the **constant of proportionality** and, in this case, it is equal to the cost per litre of the petrol. The example below is based on petrol prices in 2007.

◼ If 10 litres of petrol cost £9.50, what is the cost per litre?

☐ The cost per litre is $\dfrac{£9.50}{10}$, which is £0.95.

◼ What is the total cost of 20 litres of petrol at this price?

☐ The total cost is £0.95 × 20, which is £19.00. You could have obtained the same answer by doubling the cost of 10 litres (since you are buying twice the volume of petrol).

Note that so-called constants of proportionality, while having a constant value while the proportionality holds true, may vary in other circumstances. In the example of buying petrol, the cost per litre will vary from week to week and from petrol station to petrol station.

Proportionalities between quantities are common in science and you have already encountered a few in this course. Consider Newton's second law of motion, which can be written as $F = ma$. This means that the magnitude of the unbalanced force on an object is proportional to the magnitude of the object's acceleration or, in symbols, $F \propto a$, and m is the constant of proportionality. Provided the mass of the object can be assumed to be constant, a doubling of the force will result in a doubling of the acceleration, and so on.

The fact that the work done by a force is proportional to the size of the force can be written as:

$$W \propto F \tag{4.1}$$

where W is the work done by a force of magnitude F. If the force is doubled, the work done is doubled. If the force is halved, the work done is halved.

The work done by the force is also proportional to the distance, d, over which the force is applied, i.e.

$$W \propto d \tag{4.2}$$

◼ If a child pushes a toy train for a distance of 5 cm and on another occasion pushes the same train with the same force for a distance of 20 cm, how much greater is the work done?

☐ Since 20 cm is four times greater than 5 cm, the work done is also four times greater.

The situation here is one in which one quantity, work, is proportional to two other quantities, $W \propto F$ and $W \propto d$. Is there a single expression that includes both relationships? The answer is yes. To understand the way in which proportionalities between one quantity and two others can be combined, return to the example of purchasing petrol. Suppose you want to fill a can of petrol. Clearly, the total cost of the petrol bought is proportional to the size of the can:

$$\text{cost} \propto \text{size of can} \tag{4.3}$$

However, if you want to fill several cans of petrol, the cost is also proportional to the number of cans:

cost ∝ number of cans (4.4)

Equations 4.3 and 4.4 can be combined to give:

cost ∝ size of can × number of cans (4.5)

The following example should help to make this clear.

- It costs £4.75 to fill one 5 litre can with petrol. How much will it cost to fill three 10 litre cans?

☐ The overall cost will be £4.75 × 2 × 3 = £28.50 (£4.75 is multiplied by two because each 10 litre can contains twice as much petrol as a 5 litre one and it is multiplied by three because there are three 10 litre cans).

This method for combining proportionalities is true in all cases. It can be summarised as follows.

If a quantity a is proportional to each of a number of quantities b, c and d, i.e. if:

$a \propto b$ and $a \propto c$ and $a \propto d$

these relationships can be combined into the single proportionality relationship:

$a \propto b \times c \times d$ or $a \propto bcd$

Equations 4.1 and 4.2 can thus be combined to give:

$W \propto F \times d$ or $W \propto Fd$ (4.6)

The work done is proportional to the force, F, multiplied by the distance, d, over which the force is applied.

4.1.3 An equation for work done

The meaning of the relationship $W \propto Fd$ is illustrated in Figure 4.2. However, although this relationship tells you something about how work is related to force and distance, it doesn't give enough information to enable you to do a calculation. You first have to convert the proportionality relationship into an equation by introducing a constant of proportionality.

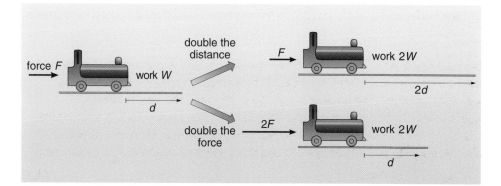

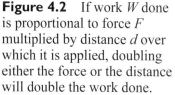

Figure 4.2 If work W done is proportional to force F multiplied by distance d over which it is applied, doubling either the force or the distance will double the work done.

29

The proportionality relationship $W \propto Fd$ can be rewritten as:

$$W = kFd \qquad (4.7)$$

where k is the constant of proportionality.

The value of the constant k depends on the units used to measure the work done. However, recall that work is the name given to the energy transferred when a force acts on an object, so the units of work are the same as the units of energy. In the SI system, the units of energy are defined so that the constant k has a value of one (and is simply a number with no units), which means that:

1 SI unit of energy = 1 SI unit of force × 1 SI unit of distance

So, provided SI units are used, Equation 4.7 can be rewritten as simply:

$$W = Fd \qquad (4.8)$$

■ You should be getting familiar with the SI units of energy and force. What are they?

□ The SI unit of energy is the joule, represented by the symbol J, and the SI unit of force is the newton, represented by the symbol N.

Although you have been using the joule as the SI unit of energy and you know that $1\,\text{J} = 1\,\text{kg m}^2\,\text{s}^{-2}$, the joule has not actually been defined yet. Equation 4.8 enables you to do this, as follows.

One joule is the energy transferred (or the work done) when a force of one newton acts for a distance of one metre.

$$1\ \text{joule} = 1\ \text{newton} \times 1\ \text{metre} \quad \text{or} \quad 1\,\text{J} = 1\,\text{N} \times 1\,\text{m} = 1\,\text{N m} \qquad (4.9)$$

■ You know that, in terms of SI base units, $1\,\text{N} = 1\,\text{kg m s}^{-2}$. Use the fact that $1\,\text{J} = 1\,\text{N} \times 1\,\text{m}$ to express 1 J in SI base units.

□ $1\,\text{J} = 1\,\text{N} \times 1\,\text{m} = 1\,\text{kg m s}^{-2} \times 1\,\text{m} = 1\,\text{kg m}^2\,\text{s}^{-2}$. Reassuringly, this is the same answer as was given in Equation 3.2.

There is one further refinement required to the definition of work: the work done depends only on the distance moved *in the direction in which the force is acting*. Consider once again the child pushing the train. If she pushes from the side, perpendicular to the direction of the track as in Figure 4.3, the train will not move in that direction (assuming that she does not push hard enough for the train to topple over). No energy is transferred to the train in this case – it is in exactly the same position as before the force was applied – and therefore no work is done on the train.

A more precise definition of work is as follows.

The work W done by a force on an object is the energy transferred to the object. For a constant force, it is equal to the magnitude F of the force multiplied by the distance d that the object moves in the direction of the force, while the force is acting on it.

$$W = Fd \qquad (4.8)$$

Figure 4.3 Pushing a train perpendicular to the direction of the track.

direction of push

Equation 4.8 can be used to calculate the work done on the train in Figure 4.1. Assume that the child pushes the train by applying a constant force of 2 N in the direction of the track over a distance of 0.3 m. Then the work done is:

$$W = Fd$$
$$= 2 \, N \times 0.3 \, m$$
$$= 0.6 \, N \, m$$

However, 1 N m = 1 J (from Equation 4.9), so the work done on the train is 0.6 J. Note that it is not wrong to quote the answer as 0.6 N m, but it is conventional to use the simpler unit, the joule, for work done or energy transferred.

■ Two sumo wrestlers push against each other with opposing forces of 1200 N, and both remain stationary (Figure 4.4). How much work is done on each wrestler?

☐ Neither wrestler moves in the direction of the force which he is experiencing, so $d = 0$. Therefore, since $W = Fd$, $W = 0$ and so no work is done on either wrestler. Note that this does *not* mean that there is no energy conversion, as both wrestlers would be at pains to point out. Chemical reactions in muscles keep them in a state of contraction, and these reactions will release stored chemical energy. As a result, the wrestlers will get rather warm!

Question 4.1

A piano is pushed across a stage by applying a force of 1.9×10^3 N for a distance of 6.5 m. How much work is done on the piano?

Question 4.1 involved calculating the work done, and hence the energy transferred, when the force and the distance moved were known. In other circumstances, you may want to calculate the force needed to transfer a certain amount of energy, or the distance that must be travelled for a known force to do a certain amount of work. Such problems require Equation 4.8 to be rearranged. Question 4.2 is one such problem and you should attempt it now. If you have difficulty with it, especially if you don't know where to start, you may find it helpful to look ahead to Activity 4.2 'Solving problems', which is at the end of this chapter.

Question 4.2

In 1957, the American strong man Paul Anderson claimed a world record that was still unbeaten 50 years later. He lifted a platform holding a total mass of 2840 kg. In doing this, he exerted a force of 2.79×10^4 N and did 2.8×10^2 J of work on the platform. Through what distance did he raise the platform?

4.2 Work and energy conservation

In considering energy conversions and transfers, it is important not to forget that work is a form of energy. The work done on an object is the energy transferred to the object, and work (in common with all types of energy) is measured in joules.

Figure 4.4 Two sumo wrestlers pushing against each other with equal and opposite forces.

$$\overset{N}{\overset{kg \, m s^{-2}}{1.9 \times 10^3}} \times 6.5m.$$

$$W \, 1.2 \times 10^4 \, Nm$$

$$W = fd.$$

$$W - 2.8 \times 10^2$$
$$F = 2.79 \times 10^4$$
$$d.$$

$$d = \frac{W}{F}$$

$$d = 0.01 \, m$$

Thinking back to the example of the toy train (and still assuming for now that the train is initially stationary, and that you can ignore friction, etc.), the law of conservation of energy tells you that in this case

> work done = increase in kinetic energy

or, in symbols:

$$W = \Delta E_k \tag{4.10}$$

Since the train is initially stationary, the increase in kinetic energy is simply the kinetic energy, $E_k = \frac{1}{2}mv^2$, possessed by the train (mass m) when it is moving at speed v after the push. In the example in Section 4.1 you found that 0.6 J of work was done when a child pushed a train by applying a force of 2 N over a distance of 0.3 m. So, on this occasion, $E_k = W = 0.6$ J.

■ If the train has a mass of 300 g, at what speed is it moving when the child stops pushing?

☐ $E_k = \frac{1}{2}mv^2$ can be rearranged, as in Section 3.3, to give an equation for v, and then you can substitute the value obtained for E_k and the value given for m. Note that the mass has been given in g not kg, so you need to start by converting 300 g to kg:

1 kg = 1×10^3 g, so 1 g = 1×10^{-3} kg and so 300 g = 300×10^{-3} kg = 0.3 kg.

It is also helpful to remember that 1 J = 1 kg m² s⁻². Then:

$$v = \sqrt{\frac{2E_k}{m}}$$

$$= \sqrt{\frac{2 \times 0.6 \text{ J}}{0.3 \text{ kg}}}$$

$$= \sqrt{\frac{2 \times 0.6 \text{ kg m}^2 \text{ s}^{-2}}{0.3 \text{ kg}}}$$

$$= \sqrt{4 \text{ m}^2 \text{ s}^{-2}}$$

$$= 2 \text{ m s}^{-1} \text{ to one significant figure}$$

remembering to take the square root of m² s⁻² as well as the number 4, and that $\sqrt{\text{m}^2 \text{ s}^{-2}} = \text{m s}^{-1}$.

Now that you have a clear picture of the relationship between force, work and kinetic energy in the simplest case, you can explore some of the assumptions made at the beginning of Section 4.1.

4.2.1   What if the train is not stationary when the force is applied?

If the force is applied when the train is already moving (Figure 4.5), you can run through similar arguments, but this time the work done by the force results in a *change* in kinetic energy. If the initial speed of the train is represented by the symbol u, and the final speed by the symbol v, its initial kinetic energy is $\frac{1}{2}mu^2$ and its final kinetic energy is $\frac{1}{2}mv^2$. So the change in kinetic energy is:

$$\Delta E_k = \tfrac{1}{2}mv^2 - \tfrac{1}{2}mu^2 \qquad\qquad (3.5)$$

as discussed in Section 3.4.

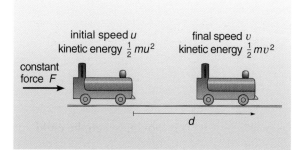

Figure 4.5   Pushing a train that was initially moving with a speed of u.

So, assuming as before that there is no friction involved, this gives:

$$W = \Delta E_k = \tfrac{1}{2}mv^2 - \tfrac{1}{2}mu^2 \qquad\qquad (4.11)$$

Question 4.3

What is the work done on a toy train (Figure 4.5) of mass 0.20 kg to increase its speed from an initial value of 1.0 m s^{-1} to a final value of 2.0 m s^{-1}?   0.3 J

4.2.2   What if there is some friction involved?

Friction was considered in Book 2, Chapter 14. In real life, when there is relative motion between two surfaces, frictional forces almost always act to oppose that motion. Frictional forces can be very useful – without them people could not park cars on hills, write with ballpoint pens or even walk along a road without falling over. Paradoxically, in a *real* train, it is the friction between the wheels and the track that enables the train to move. However, frictional forces result in energy being converted from other forms to internal energy, which results in a rise in the temperature of the moving parts. In the toy train example, this means that not all of the work done on the train is converted into kinetic energy; some is converted into internal energy.

Applying the law of conservation of energy gives:

$$\begin{pmatrix} \text{work done} \\ \text{on train} \end{pmatrix} = \begin{pmatrix} \text{change in kinetic energy} \\ \text{of train} \end{pmatrix} + \begin{pmatrix} \text{change in internal energy} \\ \text{of train} \end{pmatrix}$$

or

$$W = \Delta E_k + \Delta E_i \qquad\qquad (4.12)$$

where ΔE_i represents the change in internal energy of the train.

The magnitude of this internal energy change depends on the frictional forces. If the friction between the moving parts increases, more of the energy transferred to the train is converted into internal energy. Consequently, a smaller proportion of the energy transferred to the train is available for conversion into kinetic energy, so the train's final speed is lower.

Question 4.4

Assuming that there are frictional forces between the parts of the train, what happens to the kinetic energy of the train, and to the speed of the train, after the child has stopped pushing? *Slows, decreases*

4.2.3   What if the track is not horizontal?

If the track is horizontal, the force of gravity (which acts vertically) is perpendicular to the direction of motion. This means that the force of gravity does no work on the train and so can be ignored. However, if the track is not horizontal, the force of gravity (the subject of Chapter 5) is no longer perpendicular to the train's direction of motion and so must be taken into account.

4.3   Power

So far this book has mainly been concerned with calculating amounts of energy converted from one form into another, but it is often useful to know the *rate* at which energy is converted (or transferred). You should recall from Book 1 Section 4.1 that this is known as power. The power, P, can be calculated by dividing the energy converted, E, by the time, t, taken to do the conversion.

$$P = \frac{E}{t} \qquad\qquad (4.13)$$

In the SI system of units, power is measured in joules per second, or watts; the symbol for the watt is W, so

$$1\,W = 1\,J\,s^{-1}$$

■ Suppose that the child in Figure 4.1 transferred 0.6 J of energy to the toy train when she pushed it. What additional information do you need in order to calculate the power involved in this energy transfer?

☐ You need to know the time over which the energy was expended.

In this example, if the work was done by the child in 0.2 seconds, the mean power over that time would be:

$$P = \frac{E}{t} = \frac{0.6\,J}{0.2\,s} = 3\,J\,s^{-1} = 3\,W$$

Note that if you know the total energy converted in a given time, all you can calculate is the *mean* power used during that time. There might be all kinds of fluctuations about the mean value – but you have no way of knowing that. However, for many purposes, the mean power is a very useful quantity.

Question 4.5

An electric kettle with a power rating of 2.0 kW (2000 W) is switched on for 150 s. How much energy is transferred?

$P = \dfrac{E}{t}$ ⓔ

$E = Pt$

2000

34    $E = 2.0\,kW \times 150\,s$

$E = 300\,J$ (300,000)

4.4   Problems with problems?

The final section of this chapter is dedicated to helping to improve your confidence when tackling more complex questions (especially those involving the rearrangement and combination of equations) and to helping you to work out the correct SI units for your answers. You should start by updating your personal glossary of symbols and equations as suggested in Activity 4.1. You will use this glossary in Activity 4.2.

Activity 4.1   Keeping track of symbols, units and equations – Part 2

We expect this part of the activity will take you approximately 10 minutes.

No more new symbols, equations or units will be introduced in the rest of this chapter, but you will make extensive use of those you have already met, so you should make sure that you have included the important symbols, equations and units introduced in Chapter 4 in your glossary.

There is no 'correct' list of symbols and equations for your glossary; what you include is up to you. However, if you have difficulty in identifying the important equations from all the others, look out for those that are displayed as key points (with a background blue tone) and those listed in the chapter summaries. Thus for Chapter 4 you might reasonably include Equation 4.8 ($W = Fd$) and Equation 4.13 ($P = \dfrac{E}{t}$), along with the associated symbols and SI units.

In addition to giving the base unit equivalents of units such as the newton, the joule and the watt, you could include relationships between the units, such as $1\,\text{J} = 1\,\text{N m}$ and $1\,\text{W} = 1\,\text{J s}^{-1}$. You could also include the symbol $\propto$ with its meaning (i.e. is directly proportional to).

You are advised to continue to add new equations, symbols and SI units to your list as you study the rest of the course.

There are no comments on this activity.

Activity 4.2   Solving problems

We expect this activity will take you approximately 1 hour, including about 30 minutes studying the video sequence 'working out the units'.

Open University tutors frequently report that their students understand what is written in the course material very well, yet struggle when asked to tackle a question for themselves, especially if the question requires them to choose which equations to use, to rearrange these equations and then to substitute numerical values.

This activity requires you to answer a question that is similar in nature to many of those in this book. However, as you tackle the question you will also be developing a problem-solving strategy which you can use in subsequent questions throughout the course.

The problem-solving strategy is very simple:

1   decide how you are going to tackle the problem

2   do the calculation

3   check that your answer makes sense.

You have probably used this simple strategy many times in everyday life. For example, if you are planning a journey to a friend's house some distance away, you start by deciding how you are going to make the journey, perhaps by looking at a map or at the train timetable on the internet. Then you make the journey, not forgetting to buy your ticket or fuel for your car, following the plan you devised previously. You may wonder about the relevance of 'checking that your answer makes sense' but, in fact, you do this all the time, usually during the journey – and people react very quickly if they realise they are heading in the wrong direction!

Each of the steps in this problem-solving strategy are considered in a little more detail below, in the context of a specific question about work, energy and power.

1   Decide how you are going to tackle the problem

The best first step is to read the question really carefully, writing down what you have been asked to find and also what information you have been given. It can sometimes be helpful to draw a diagram to summarise the situation described in the question.

An example question is given below. Read it now and note down, using a diagram if you think it would help:

(a) what you have been asked to find

(b) what information you have been given in the question.

> A man pushes his broken-down car with a force of 415 N for a distance of 18 m and this takes 36 seconds. What is the mean power transferred during this time?

Now think about the other resources available to help you solve the problem. In particular, what equations might be useful? Write them down. This is where your glossary of symbols and equations will be useful. It doesn't matter if you don't use all the equations that you have written down. You should also write down any assumptions that it is reasonable to make.

Now, without doing the actual calculation, plan how you will use the information, equations and assumptions that you have written down to solve the problem. This is a particularly useful stage – don't be tempted to start rearranging equations and substituting values until you have planned your way right through the problem.

Before proceeding you might like to check your plan with the one given in the comments on this activity at the end of this book.

2   Do the calculation

Now follow your plan and do whatever algebra and arithmetic is necessary to get an answer to the question.

If your preparation was good, this stage should be relatively straightforward. However, do take care to write down all the steps of the calculation. This will help you – and other people – to understand your method. Remember that the symbol '=' means 'is equal to' (Book 1, Box 4.1) and should never be used to mean thus or therefore. It can make a calculation clearer if you align the equals symbols vertically (as is done in many of the answers at the end of this book) to indicate that the quantity on the left-hand side is equal to each of the quantities on the right-hand side. It can also be very helpful to include words of explanation in your working – it doesn't all have to be symbols and numbers.

Don't forget to give your answer to an appropriate number of significant figures.

■ When multiplying and dividing numbers, what is the guideline for the appropriate number of significant figures in the final answer?

☐ The number of significant figures in the final answer should be the same as in the given value with the fewest significant figures (Book 1, Section 3.1.4).

When solving problems, you will sometimes get to the answer by a series of steps. If you round your answer to the required number of significant figures at each step, you may get a **rounding error** in your result.

For example, imagine that you have been asked to divide 6.0 by 4.1 and then to square the answer. Clearly, the final answer should be given to two significant figures. The intermediate step is $\frac{6.0}{4.1} = 1.463\,414\,634\ldots$ Squaring this gives 2.141 582 391, i.e. 2.1 to two significant figures. However, if you rounded the intermediate result to two significant figures, you would square 1.5, which gives 2.25, that is 2.3 to two significant figures – a different answer.

To avoid rounding errors you are advised to keep at least one additional digit in your intermediate answers (so in this case you might square 1.46 which gives 2.1316, once again 2.1 to two significant figures). Don't forget to round to an appropriate number of significant figures right at the end of the calculation.

You should also take particular care over the units associated with the values you have been given and the units of your final answer. The video sequence *Working out the Units* which accompanies this activity gives more advice on this.

3   Check that your answer makes sense

You may know from everyday experience whether your answer seems reasonable. If you found the height of a table to be 10 km or the mass of a person to be 3 g (3×10^{-3} kg) then you would realise that you had made a mistake. However, everyday experience won't always help – you are probably not familiar with the power of a man pushing a car (although if your answer turned out to be, say, 5×10^{27} W, which is more than the power of the Sun, you might be a little suspicious!).

There are various other ways in which you can check that your answer is reasonable. None of these will guarantee that your answer is correct but they will frequently highlight when mistakes have been made.

It is very easy to make a mistake when using your calculator, but most of the calculations in this course don't use numbers that are easy to check without your calculator. However, you can check that your answer is *approximately* correct by using numbers that are of a similar size but rather easier to handle. For example, in the question you have been answering, try repeating the calculation with the approximate values of $F \approx 400$ N, $d \approx 20$ m and $t \approx 40$ s (the symbol '$\approx$' means 'is approximately equal to'). Try to do this without using your calculator. Is your answer of a similar size to the one you found previously?

If you have written the units down at each stage of your working and worked out the units of the final answer, rather than just assuming them to be the units you were expecting, you can use this as a method for checking your working.

■ In the example you have calculated the mean power of a man pushing a car. What would you expect the units of the final answer to be?

☐ The units will be watts (symbol W), where $1 \text{ W} = 1 \text{ J s}^{-1}$ (see Section 4.3).

A complete answer to the example question is given in the comments on this activity at the end of this book, and the problem-solving strategy is summarised below.

1   Decide how you are going to tackle the problem

Read the question.

Write down what you are trying to find.

Write down what information you have been given.

Draw a diagram if that would help.

Which equations could you use?

What assumptions could you make?

Plan the steps needed to get to an answer.

2   Do the calculation

Rearrange the equations and substitute values.

Take care to write down your working carefully.

Give your answer to an appropriate number of significant figures.

Take particular care with units.

3   Check that your answer makes sense

Is the answer reasonable?

Check your working using approximate values.

Do the units work out as expected?

You should now watch the video sequence *Working out the Units*. You may find it helpful to watch the video sequence once without stopping and then replay it, pausing from time to time to check your understanding.

As the problem-solving strategy becomes more familiar, you will probably find that you are using it without much thought, and you should find it becomes easier to answer questions. Question 4.6 provides an opportunity for you to practise your problem-solving strategy and the answer at the end of the book tackles the question in this way. You should continue to practise your problem-solving skills in Chapter 5.

Question 4.6

A stationary golf ball of mass 5.0×10^{-2} kg is struck by a club, which gives it a speed of 75 m s^{-1}. If the mean power used during the contact between club and ball is 3.1 kW, calculate the length of time for which ball and club are in contact.

4.5　Summary of Chapter 4

The work W done by a force on an object is equal to the magnitude of the force F multiplied by the distance d that the object moves in the direction of the force while the force is acting on it, i.e. $W = Fd$.

The work done on an object is equal to the energy transferred to that object.

One joule is the energy transferred when a force of one newton acts for a distance of one metre, i.e. 1 J = 1 N m.

Power P is the rate at which energy E is converted or transferred, and is given by $P = \dfrac{E}{t}$. The SI unit of power is the watt: 1 W = 1 J s^{-1}.

Two quantities are directly proportional to each other if, when the value of one is multiplied (or divided) by a certain amount, the value of the other also becomes multiplied (or divided) by the same amount. The symbol $\propto$ means is proportional to.

If $a \propto b$, and $a \propto c$, then $a \propto bc$. Also, $a = kbc$, where k is a constant of proportionality.

In studying this chapter you have started a personal glossary of symbols, units and equalities. You have developed a strategy for solving mathematical problems and have learned how to work out what the units of your final answer should be.

When answering questions it is useful to plan your method *before* rearranging equations and substituting values, and to check that your answer makes sense.

To avoid rounding errors you should keep at least one additional digit in intermediate answers.

It is important to quote the correct unit with any quantity. If you substitute values into an equation in the correct SI units, the unit of the answer will be the SI unit of the quantity calculated. Checking the unit of your answer is a way of checking that your method is reasonable.

Chapter 5
Motion under gravity

The gravitational force of attraction between objects was introduced in Book 2. You also learned that this force is the reason you feel yourself pulled towards the Earth's surface.

■ How does the magnitude of the gravitational force between two objects change when the masses of the objects increase, and when their separation increases?

□ The magnitude of the gravitational force increases when the masses of the objects increase, and it decreases as their separation increases (Book 2, Section 14.4).

Consider the gravitational force experienced by an object on the Earth's surface. The object might be a person – you. The Earth is approximately spherical and the gravitational force acts as if all of the Earth's mass is at its centre. So the separation between the object and the centre of the Earth is essentially the same for all objects at or close to the Earth's surface.

■ Does this mean that every object on the Earth's surface experiences the same gravitational force?

□ No. The force experienced also depends on the mass of the object.

In fact, the gravitational force, F_g, experienced by an object is directly proportional to its mass, m, so you can write:

$$F_g \propto m$$

Thus the force of gravity you experience on Earth is proportional to your own mass. Someone with a mass of 50 kg experiences only half the gravitational force felt by someone with a mass of 100 kg.

■ How can this relationship between gravitational force and mass be expressed as an algebraic equation?

□ A proportionality relationship between two quantities can be changed into an equation by introducing a constant of proportionality.

In this case, the equation linking the gravitational force F_g with the mass m that experiences the force can be written as:

$$F_g = \text{constant} \times m$$

or, using the symbol g to represent the constant of proportionality:

$$F_g = g \times m$$

or simply

$$F_g = gm \qquad\qquad (5.1)$$

■ What are the units of the constant of proportionality, g?

□ Equation 5.1 can be written as $gm = F_g$ and then rearranged (by dividing both sides by m) to give:

$$g = \frac{F_g}{m}$$

F_g is a force, measured in newtons and m is a mass measured in kg, so the units of g are $\frac{N}{kg}$ or N kg^{-1}.

Alternatively, you could use the fact that 1 N = 1 kg m s^{-2} to say that the units of g are $\frac{kg\ m\ s^{-2}}{kg}$, or simply m s^{-2}.

5.1   Acceleration due to gravity

To discover more about the meaning of the constant g in Equation 5.1, consider the motion of an object of mass m which is falling towards the Earth; for example, an apple falling from a tree. Newton's second law of motion states that the acceleration a of the object is related to the unbalanced force F acting on it by the equation:

$$F = ma \tag{5.2}$$

If the force due to air resistance is assumed to be small enough to be neglected, the object falls freely, under the influence of the gravitational force F_g only. So the unbalanced force, F, in Equation 5.2 must be F_g and in this case, Newton's second law for a freely falling object can be written as:

$$F_g = ma \tag{5.3}$$

You now have two equations for F_g (Equations 5.3 and 5.1), so you can equate the right-hand sides as follows:

$$ma = gm \tag{5.4}$$

Dividing both sides of Equation 5.4 by m leads to an important conclusion about the acceleration a of an object acted on by the force of gravity alone:

$$a = g \tag{5.5}$$

where g is a constant.

The **acceleration due to gravity** experienced by any object that is falling freely close to the Earth's surface is a constant. It has the same value, irrespective of the mass of the object.

The fact that the acceleration due to gravity does not depend on the mass of the object has a remarkable consequence. It means that, provided air resistance can be ignored, two objects dropped from the same height will fall at the same rate and so hit the ground at the same time, irrespective of their mass. According to folklore, the Italian mathematician Galileo Galilei (1564–1642) tested this result by dropping cannonballs of different mass from the Leaning Tower of Pisa (Figure 5.1a). Galileo probably did not perform this experiment but the result was undoubtedly confirmed by an experiment carried out by David Scott, the commander of the crew of *Apollo 15*, on the surface of the Moon on 2 August 1971. He dropped a hammer and a feather at the same time (Figure 5.1b) and they hit the ground at the same time. If this experiment had been carried out on Earth, air resistance would have caused the feather to fall more slowly, but air resistance on the Moon's surface is negligible and so, in Scott's words, 'How about that! Mr Galileo was correct in his findings.'

(a) (b)

Figure 5.1 (a) Galileo's experiment, showing that cannonballs of different mass are accelerated equally by gravity and so fall at the same rate. Historians doubt that Galileo performed this experiment, although he certainly proposed that gravity pulls large and small objects towards the Earth with the same acceleration. His proposal was so contentious at the time that he was forced to leave the University of Pisa. (b) Confirmation of Galileo's predictions came when an astronaut demonstrated that a feather and a hammer, dropped from the same height and at the same time, hit the surface of the Moon at the same time.

The constant of proportionality that was introduced in Equation 5.1 is always represented by the symbol g. It is commonly referred to as 'the acceleration due to gravity' and recall that its units can be expressed as either N kg^{-1} or m s^{-2} where m s^{-2} are, as you learned in Book 2, Section 14.1.3, the SI units of acceleration. However, although we have only considered the effect of gravity on a freely falling object, Equation 5.1 is completely general and applies even when an object is not moving. The gravitational force F_g experienced by an object is called the **weight** of the object and Equation 5.1 can be rewritten as:

$$F_g = mg \quad \text{or} \quad \text{weight} = mg \tag{5.6}$$

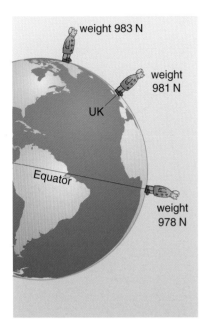

weight 983 N

weight 981 N

UK

Equator

weight 978 N

Figure 5.2 The variation of the acceleration due to gravity means that the weight of a person depends on their location on Earth. A person with a mass of 100 kg will have a weight of about 981 N in the UK, but at the Equator this will be reduced to 978 N and at the North Pole it will be 983 N. Note that this variation is small. At all three locations the person's weight is 9.8×10^2 N (and $g = 9.8$ m s^{-2}) to two significant figures.

Remember that, although the words mass and weight are used to mean the same thing in everyday speech, in science they have different meanings. Weight is a force (measured in newtons) whereas mass can be considered to be a measure of how much matter an object contains (measured in kilograms).

The symbol g was introduced as a constant of proportionality. However, its value on the Earth's surface is only approximately constant; it varies slightly, depending on altitude and latitude. The value of g is 0.5% greater at the Poles than at the Equator, and there are two reasons for this; one is the slightly non-spherical shape of the Earth and the other is the Earth's rotation. However, for the purposes of this course, the small variations will usually be ignored and the value of the acceleration due to gravity near to the Earth's surface will be taken to be 9.8 m s^{-2}. The value of the acceleration due to gravity on the Moon is only about one-sixth of the Earth's value. This is because the Moon has a different size and mass. The variation in g means that, whereas the mass m of an object is constant (provided it does not lose or gain matter), its weight F_g depends on where on the Earth (Figure 5.2) or in the Universe the object is located.

Question 5.1

What is the weight of a person with a mass of 76 kg (a) on the Earth (assuming $g = 9.8$ m s^{-2}) and (b) on the Moon where the acceleration due to gravity is roughly 1.6 m s^{-2}?

5.2 Work done by gravity

Ideas from Chapter 4 can be used to calculate the work done by the gravitational force on a falling object. Adopting the same simplifying approach as in Chapter 4, start by assuming that air resistance is negligible. This is similar to the assumption of zero friction in the toy train example (Section 4.1). In fact, air resistance *is* negligible for many practical purposes, so the calculations here won't be too unrealistic.

From the definition of work in Section 4.1.1, you should be able to see that if an object falls a certain distance, work will be done on it by the gravitational force that is acting on it. This work will cause the kinetic energy of the object to increase as it falls, just as the work done on the train causes its kinetic energy to increase. It is easy enough to calculate the energy involved. Imagine a book falling from a table onto the floor (Figure 5.3). To calculate the work done on the book, you simply need to know the force (the weight of the book) and the distance travelled in the direction of the force (the height of the table).

■ Suppose that the book has a mass m, and the table top is a distance h above the floor. Write down an equation for the work W done by gravity on the book as it falls from the table top to the floor.

□ Work done $W = Fd$. In this case the force on the book is the weight, so $F = F_g = mg$, and the distance moved is the table height, so $d = h$. Thus:

$$W = mgh \qquad (5.7)$$

$F_g = mg$

Figure 5.3 A falling book.

In the next question you are asked to *estimate* the work done when one of your course books falls to the floor. To do this, you need to estimate the mass of the book and the height of your table. That means you are *not* expected to use exact measured values but, rather, to make 'educated guesses'. For example, you might pick up this book and think how its mass compares with that of a 1 kg bag of sugar or the mass of some other object of known mass. Similarly, you could compare the height of the table with your height. You should also round the value of g to 10 m s^{-2}, since your estimates of mass and height will only justify quoting the estimated work done to one significant figure.

Estimating is a useful skill to acquire as it gives you practice in doing rough calculations, which can also be helpful in checking the answers given by your calculator by using approximate values (as discussed in Activity 4.2). In addition, making sensible estimates with approximate values gives you a feel for the size of units such as the joule and the newton.

Question 5.2

(a) Estimate the work done on an S104 course book by gravity if you let it fall from your table to the floor?

(b) Assuming that air resistance is negligible, what is the kinetic energy of the book just before it hits the floor, and what is its speed at this point?

(c) What happens to this kinetic energy when the book hits the floor?

5.3 Work done against gravity – gravitational potential energy

Now consider the work done when an object is lifted. To lift an object with a mass m, you have to apply an upward force of at least mg to overcome the downward force of gravity. If this force raises the object through a height h, the work done is:

$$W = Fd = mg \times h = mgh$$

So, if an object of mass m is raised through a height h, the work done on the object is equal to mgh, and so this amount of energy is transferred to the object. (Note that this equation is identical to the one describing an object falling under gravity – Equation 5.7.)

Of course, this ties in very well with everyday observations. If you lift a heavy suitcase onto a luggage rack in a train, or a heavy bag of shopping onto a table, you are very aware that you are doing work against gravity. You will also be aware that more work is required to lift a more massive object, or the same object to a greater height, and these observations are consistent with the work done being equal to mgh.

■ Calculate the work done in lifting a 12 kg suitcase from floor level up to a luggage rack 2.0 m above the floor (Figure 5.4a).

□ The work done is $W = mgh$, so

$$W = 12 \text{ kg} \times 9.8 \text{ m s}^{-2} \times 2.0 \text{ m}$$
$$= 235.2 \text{ kg m}^2 \text{ s}^{-2}$$
$$= 2.4 \times 10^2 \text{ J to two significant figures}$$

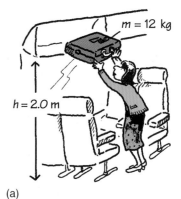

(a)

(b)

Figure 5.4 (a) Placing a suitcase on a luggage rack involves doing work against gravity. (b) The stored energy is released if the suitcase falls off the rack.

■ When the suitcase is on the luggage rack, what has happened to the 240 J of energy that was supplied to lift it? According to the law of conservation of energy, energy can't just disappear. When work was done on the toy train in Chapter 4, the energy supplied was converted into kinetic energy (and some internal energy when friction was taken into account), yet a suitcase placed on a luggage rack is obviously stationary.

☐ The work done has been converted into gravitational potential energy. Recall from Chapter 2 that potential energy is stored energy, and the term potential signifies that this energy has the potential to 'make things happen' at a later stage. Consider what happens if the suitcase falls from the rack. As it falls, the energy reappears as kinetic energy, and the instant before it hits the floor the 240 J will be present as kinetic energy (Figure 5.4b). In other words, when the suitcase was lifted, energy was stored and released as kinetic energy when the case fell back down.

In general, when an object is raised to a greater height, work is done on the object and the energy transferred is stored; the amount of energy stored is $mg\Delta h$, where Δh is the change in height.

In all problems involving gravitational potential energy, it is the *changes* of energy that are important. A change of height leads to a change of gravitational potential energy; the absolute value of the gravitational potential energy is unimportant. So if the 12 kg suitcase is dropped through 2 m in a room at the top of a tower block, it will have the same kinetic energy, and the same speed, just before it hits the floor as when it falls 2 m from the luggage rack to the floor of a train. In neither instance can you say that the suitcase has no gravitational potential energy after falling, since you could push it off a balcony, or out of a train, and its gravitational potential energy would decrease further as it fell further.

The fact that it is changes in height and gravitational potential energy that are important can be emphasised by writing an equation for gravitational potential energy in terms of changes:

change in gravitational potential energy = $mg \times$ change in height

or, using the Δ (delta) notation which was introduced in Section 3.4:

$$\Delta E_g = mg\Delta h \tag{5.8}$$

Remember that ΔE_g means the change in E_g, and Δh means the change in h. Clearly, when an object is raised to a greater height, its gravitational potential energy increases and, when it falls to a lower height, its gravitational potential energy decreases. So a negative value of Δh leads to a negative value of ΔE_g.

5.4 Gravitational potential energy and energy conservation

The concept of gravitational potential energy greatly simplifies calculations concerned with the effect of gravity on the motion of objects, particularly where no other forces are concerned. For example, if you take your course book and throw it vertically upwards in the air, it will slow down as it travels higher, and eventually reach a point where it is momentarily stationary. It will then accelerate downwards to the place where you are waiting to catch it (before it hits the ground). By using the idea of the change in gravitational potential energy, coupled with the law of conservation of energy, quantities such as the speed of the book at a given height and the maximum height it will reach can be calculated. These calculations assume that no air resistance acts on the book after it is thrown, so, in accordance with the law of conservation of energy, the sum of its kinetic energy and its gravitational potential energy must be constant. To put this another way: any increase in gravitational potential energy is accompanied by a decrease in kinetic energy of equal size, and vice versa.

Consider a book of mass m, thrown vertically upwards with an initial speed u. After it has risen through a height Δh it has a speed v.

■ What is the increase in gravitational potential energy of the book?

☐ From Equation 5.8, the increase in gravitational potential energy is equal to $mg\Delta h$.

(a)

■ What is the decrease in kinetic energy of the book?

☐ The book's initial kinetic energy is $\frac{1}{2}mu^2$ and its final kinetic energy is $\frac{1}{2}mv^2$; so the decrease in kinetic energy is $\frac{1}{2}mu^2 - \frac{1}{2}mv^2$. (Note that this is a *decrease* in kinetic energy, since the initial speed u is greater than the final speed v.)

Since energy is conserved, the increase in gravitational potential energy must be equal to the decrease in kinetic energy, giving the following equation:

$$mg\Delta h = \tfrac{1}{2}mu^2 - \tfrac{1}{2}mv^2 \qquad (5.9)$$

Of course, this equation doesn't apply only to books; it also applies to the movement of any object when gravity is the sole force acting on it.

(b)

Another common example of conversion between kinetic energy and gravitational energy is a child's swing (Figure 5.5a).

■ At which point(s) during the motion of the swing will the gravitational potential energy have a maximum value, and at which point(s) will it have a minimum value?

☐ The gravitational potential energy must be at a maximum at the two highest points of the swing cycle and at a minimum at the lowest point of the cycle.

Figure 5.5 (a) Motion of a swing during its swing cycle. (b) An extra energy input is needed from a push in order to combat the effects of friction.

Figure 5.6 A huge pendulum bob suspended from the dome of St Paul's Cathedral in London for an Open University television programme filmed in 1978. Presented by Professor Mike Pentz (1924–1995), who is seen on the left and was the first Dean of Science at The Open University, the programme demonstrated that the plane in which the pendulum swung actually rotated relative to the Cathedral, because of the daily rotation of the Earth. Using a massive pendulum bob reduced the proportion of the energy of the pendulum that was converted into internal energy by air resistance forces during each swing.

■ At which points(s) during the motion of the swing will the kinetic energy have a minimum value, and at which point(s) will it have a maximum value?

☐ Kinetic energy will be at a minimum value when the speed is at a minimum. This will occur at the highest points in the swing cycle, where the swing stops momentarily before reversing direction. Conversely, kinetic energy will be at a maximum when the speed is greatest – which is at the lowest point in the swing cycle shown in Figure 5.5a.

The previous point also follows from the law of conservation of energy. If friction and air resistance are negligible, the total energy E_{tot} is the sum of the kinetic energy E_k and the gravitational potential energy E_g:

$$E_{tot} = E_k + E_g \tag{5.10}$$

E_{tot} must be constant because energy is conserved. So the kinetic energy will be at a maximum when the gravitational potential energy is at a minimum and vice versa. This leads to exactly the same conclusion that was reached based on your experience of how the speed of a swing varies.

If there is no friction or air resistance gradually converting the available energy into internal energy, the swing would go backwards and forwards for ever, converting gravitational potential energy into kinetic energy and back again. However, for any real swing, there is always friction at the point of suspension, as well as air resistance during the swing's motion. Thus some of the kinetic energy is converted into internal energy in the swing and its surroundings. For this reason a swing always comes to a halt in the absence of external forces – which is why someone is needed to push the swing in order to provide extra energy to maintain its motion (Figure 5.5b).

The above discussion applies equally well to the motion of a pendulum. The conversion of kinetic energy into internal energy due to frictional forces can be made relatively small by using a pendulum bob with a very large mass and suspending it from a very long cable (Figure 5.6).

Question 5.3

Figure 5.6 shows an enormous pendulum in St Paul's Cathedral in London. The pendulum bob had a mass of 80 kg, the suspension cable was 82 m long, and the bob swung back and forth through a distance of 6 m. If the height difference between the highest and lowest points in the bob's motion is 5.5 cm, calculate (a) the change in gravitational potential energy of the bob between these points, and (b) the maximum speed reached by the bob.

Gravitational potential energy has many applications. The energy stored by water behind a dam is a case in point (Figure 5.7). The controlled release of that energy, by allowing the water to descend through turbines, produces hydroelectricity that is important in many regions of the world. It is hoped that hydroelectricity from the Three Gorges Dam across the Yangtze River will contribute 4% of China's total electricity needs when the dam is fully operational in 2009.

Figure 5.7 The dam for the hydroelectric power station at Glen Canyon, Utah, USA.

In addition to its usefulness in generating electricity, the gravitational potential energy associated with water stored at height is used in pumped storage schemes to enable electricity to be made available at times of peak demand. Pumped storage schemes, such as the one at Dinorwig in North Wales, have two reservoirs, one at a greater height than the other (Figure 5.8). Electrical energy is used to pump water to the top reservoir when demand for electricity from consumers is low (e.g. late at night). Then, when demand for electricity is high, water is allowed to flow back down the tunnels to drive the turbines and hence to generate electricity.

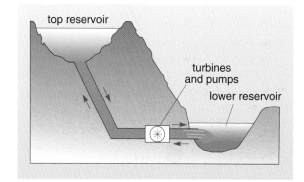

Figure 5.8 A plan of the Dinorwig Pumped Storage Scheme. Note that most of the pipes, turbines and pumps are deep inside a mountain, so very little is visible to a passer-by.

5.5   Other forms of potential energy

It is worth emphasising that the gravitational potential energy of an object increases when it moves in the opposite direction to the gravitational force (that is, when it moves upwards). This relationship between energy and force does not only apply to gravity. For many forces, motion *against* the force (that is, in the opposite direction to the force) allows energy to be stored, and this energy can be reclaimed when the object is allowed to move in the direction of the force. So, as mentioned in Chapter 2, gravitational potential energy is not the only useful type of potential energy.

An important example of potential energy is the energy stored within an object when it is stretched, or squashed or otherwise deformed. Recall from Chapter 2 that this kind of potential energy is called strain potential energy and it has applications in trampolines and bouncing balls. Strain potential energy is also used in old-fashioned clocks and watches and in wind-up 'clockwork' toys (Figure 5.9) where energy is frequently stored in a spring.

If you compress or extend a spring, you do work against the force that the spring exerts to try to maintain its natural length. The energy stored in the spring depends on the change in length of the spring – or on the distance that the end of the spring is moved relative to its natural, undeformed position (Figure 5.10). When you release the spring, the stored strain energy is converted into kinetic energy.

Figure 5.9   A wind-up toy. Turning the key causes energy to be stored as strain potential energy in a spring. This is then converted into kinetic energy as the toy moves across the table.

The distinguishing feature of potential energy in all its forms is that it depends on the *position* of an object and not on its motion. Thus gravitational (potential) energy depends on the height of an object, and strain (potential) energy depends on the compression (or extension) of an object. Other forms of potential energy are discussed in Chapters 6 and 7.

5.6   Combining equations

Look at Question 5.3 and your answer to it. You started by using $\Delta E = mg\Delta h$ to find the change in gravitational potential energy of the pendulum bob. Then you used the conservation of energy to say that the maximum kinetic energy of the bob was equal to the change in gravitational potential energy, that is:

$$E_k = \tfrac{1}{2}mv^2 = \Delta E_g$$

where v was the maximum speed of the bob, the quantity you were trying to find in the second part of the question. Rearranging this equation and substituting values for m and ΔE_g led to a value for v.

There is a more direct method for reaching the final answer to this question, without calculating the change in gravitational potential energy of the pendulum bob. Since $\Delta E_g = mg\Delta h$ and also $\Delta E_g = \tfrac{1}{2}mv^2$ in this case, you can write:

$$mg\Delta h = \tfrac{1}{2}mv^2 \tag{5.11}$$

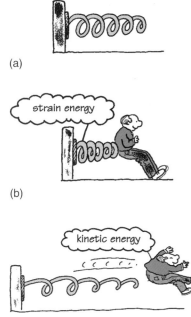

Figure 5.10   (a) A spring in its natural, undeformed state. (b) When work is done to compress the spring, energy is stored in the spring as strain energy. (c) When the spring is released, strain energy is converted into kinetic energy.

■   What do you notice about the terms for mass in Equation 5.11?

☐   There is a mass term m on both sides of the equation.

So, remembering from Section 3.3 that you can do almost anything to one side of an equation provided you do the same thing to the other side of the equation, you can divide both sides of Equation 5.11 by m to give:

$$g\Delta h = \tfrac{1}{2}v^2$$

Reversing this equation gives:

$$\tfrac{1}{2}v^2 = g\Delta h$$

Multiplying both sides by 2 gives:

$$v^2 = 2g\Delta h$$

Taking the square root of both sides gives:

$$v = \sqrt{2g\Delta h}$$

Substituting values of $g = 9.8$ m s^{-2} and $\Delta h = 0.055$ m gives:

$$v = \sqrt{2 \times 9.8 \text{ m s}^{-2} \times 0.055 \text{ m}}$$
$$= \sqrt{1.078 \text{ m}^2 \text{ s}^{-2}}$$
$$= 1.0 \text{ m s}^{-1} \text{ to two significant figures}$$

This is the same answer as obtained previously but it was obtained much more directly – and without needing to substitute a value for the mass of the pendulum bob.

This example illustrates the benefits of combining and rearranging equations before substituting numerical values. In addition to being more direct, it makes it easier to spot mistakes. If you substitute a lot of numbers and units in an equation before you rearrange it, it can be very easy to lose track of where you are up to in the calculation – and errors can be difficult to spot.

Combining two equations as done here has some additional benefits:

* Since you are not calculating an intermediate value (ΔE_g in this case), there is less danger of rounding errors being introduced.
* Some symbols or numbers may cancel out (as the m terms did here), thus simplifying the final calculation.
* It is easier to see how one quantity depends on another. For example, the pendulum bob's maximum speed is proportional to the square root of the height difference between its highest and lowest points. Interestingly, the maximum speed of the bob does not depend on its mass at all.

So, wherever possible, you should combine and rearrange equations *before* substituting numerical values.

Sometimes equations can be combined simply by setting one equation equal to another one, as in the example of the pendulum bob. In other cases you may need to substitute the symbols from one equation into another one. Suppose you want to calculate the power of something from given values of force, distance moved in the direction of the force, and time, as you did in Activity 4.2. In the answer for that activity, $W = Fd$ was used to find the work done and then this value and $P = \dfrac{E}{t}$ were used to find power (since $E = W$ in this case). However, you could avoid the need to calculate a value for W by writing Fd instead of E in the equation for power:

$$P = \frac{E}{t} = \frac{Fd}{t}$$

Then you could substitute values for F, d and t to find P directly:

$$P = \frac{Fd}{t}$$
$$= \frac{415\,\text{N} \times 18\,\text{m}}{36\,\text{s}}$$
$$= \frac{415 \times 18\,\text{N m}}{36\,\text{s}}$$
$$= 207.5\,\text{J s}^{-1}$$
$$= 2.1 \times 10^2\,\text{W to two significant figures, as previously}$$

Activity 5.1   Manipulating algebra in problems

We expect this activity will take you approximately 15 minutes.

The problem-solving strategy developed in Activity 4.2 suggested that you should 'do the calculation' by 'rearranging the equations and substituting values'. When doing this, you now should bear in mind the additional advice to combine and rearrange equations *before* substituting values.

Use your modified problem-solving strategy to tackle the following question:

> A diver who dives off the famous cliffs at Acapulco in Mexico hits the water at about 25 m s^{-1}. Calculate the height of the cliff.

Why is your answer likely to be an underestimate? (*Hint*: think about what assumption you made to calculate the height.)

Now look at the comments on this activity at the end of this book.

Question 5.4

In the sport of ski-jumping, skiers descend a steep ramp before launching themselves off the end of it (Figure 5.11). If a skier starts from rest and the vertical drop of the ramp is 50 m, at what speed is he travelling when he leaves the ramp? What assumptions have you made in arriving at your answer?

Figure 5.11 A ski-jumper descending a ramp before launching himself off the end of it. The aim is to travel as far as possible from the end of the ramp.

5.7 Summary of Chapter 5

All objects, irrespective of their mass, experience the same acceleration g when falling freely under the influence of gravity at the same point on the Earth. Close to the Earth's surface, $g = 9.8$ m s^{-2}. The weight of an object is the force, F_g, due to gravity acting on the object, and for an object with mass m the weight is given by $F_g = mg$.

If the height of an object of mass m changes by Δh, the change in gravitational potential energy is $\Delta E_g = mg\Delta h$.

If gravity is the only force acting on an object, the sum of kinetic energy and gravitational potential energy is constant. Increases in kinetic energy are balanced by decreases in gravitational potential energy, and vice versa.

There are various forms of potential energy, all of which depend on the position of an object rather than on its motion. The potential energy of an object increases as it moves in the opposite direction to that of the force acting on it. Strain potential energy depends on the extension or compression of an object.

In studying this chapter you have estimated values and you have also combined algebraic equations together.

It is good practice to combine and rearrange equations before substituting numerical values.

Chapter 6
Internal energy, heat transfer and temperature change

In real-life examples of energy conversion or transfer, the objects involved and their surroundings frequently become warmer, indicating that some of the energy is converted into internal energy. Why is this the case? What exactly is internal energy anyway, and how can the internal energy of an object be altered? What are the differences between internal energy, heat and temperature? This chapter will answer these questions. You will also have the opportunity to make some practical measurements relating to internal energy changes, and you will learn how to write up an experimental report.

6.1 What is internal energy?

As the name suggests, internal energy is the energy contained *within* a substance. To understand this, consider the particles of which solids, liquids and gases are composed. You know from Book 1, Section 5.1 that the particles in gases move about continually. In fact, whether the substance is a solid, a liquid or a gas, the particles (usually molecules) are in continual random motion.

In the solid state (Figure 6.1a) the particles are packed closely together and they have fixed positions relative to each other. They do not swap places, but they do vibrate about their fixed positions, as indicated by Figure 6.1a. In the liquid state (Figure 6.1b), molecules are not arranged in a regular way and they move around, jostling and swapping places. In the gaseous state (Figure 6.1c), the molecules are much further apart and move around rapidly in a random, chaotic manner, frequently colliding and bouncing off each other and the walls of the container.

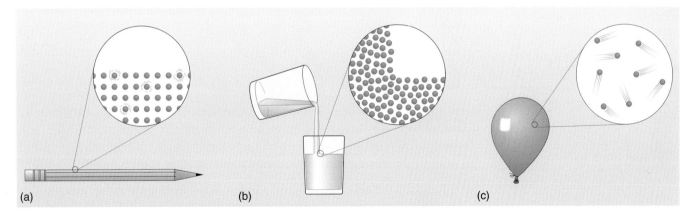

(a)   (b)   (c)

Figure 6.1 The arrangement of particles in the (a) solid, (b) liquid and (c) gaseous state. Note that in all three states all the particles are in continual motion.

In all three states the particles have a wide range of speeds, and their speeds are continually changing as a result of either collisions or interactions. However, the *mean* speed is related to the temperature. As the temperature increases, the mean

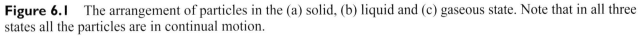

55

speed of the particles increases. The mean kinetic energy must increase too, since kinetic energy is proportional to the square of the speed. This kinetic energy associated with the random motion of particles is one component of the internal energy of any object. So when an object's temperature is increased, its internal energy is increased too.

The other component of the internal energy of an object is associated with the potential energy of the particles; stored energy that is associated with the forces that bind atoms together into molecules, and that bind molecules together in the solid and liquid states. This potential energy is primarily electrical in origin (you will consider electrical energy in Chapter 7). Within any object there is a huge number of molecules, and each of them will be attracted to all of its neighbours, so there will be a huge number of molecular potential energies.

> The total **internal energy** of an object is the sum of the kinetic and potential energies of all of the molecules in the object.

Internal energy can also be altered by changing the state of a substance, for example, by the evaporation of a liquid. The separation of the molecules in a gas is generally far larger than in a liquid, so work has to be done on the molecules to increase their separation, and this leads to an increase in their potential energy. As a result, the internal energy of a gas at the boiling temperature is greater than the internal energy of the same mass of the liquid at the same temperature. The kinetic energy associated with the random motion of the molecules is essentially the same for the gas and for the liquid since they are at the same temperature, but the potential energy of the molecules in the gas is higher than the potential energy of the molecules in the liquid.

Chemical energy is another form of internal energy. It is released, for example, when fuel is burned or in biochemical processes in living organisms. In a chemical reaction, atoms swap partners, so the molecules produced in a chemical reaction are made up of atoms linked in different ways from those in the reacting molecules. This means that the potential energy associated with forces between neighbouring atoms is different. Chemical energy is discussed in more detail in Book 4.

6.2   Increasing internal energy by friction or heating

Recall that whenever work is done against air resistance or friction, there is an increase in internal energy. The increase in temperature associated with this can be substantial; for example, when a spacecraft returns to Earth through the atmosphere, its surface temperature increases to around 2000 °C.

Why does the internal energy increase in this way? As the spacecraft travels through the atmosphere, it displaces molecules in the air from its path and so there is a huge number of collisions between the molecules on the spacecraft's surface and molecules in the air. These molecular collisions constitute a force on the spacecraft, which is usually described as being caused by air resistance. This force does work on the spacecraft as it moves through the air and it results in an increase in the internal energy of both the spacecraft and the air, so both get warmer. The increases in internal energy exactly balance the decrease in the sum of the kinetic energy and the gravitational potential energy of the spacecraft as a whole, so the total amount of energy is conserved.

Air resistance and friction are always present to some extent on Earth which means that kinetic energy is always being converted into internal energy. So moving objects always slow down and eventually stop, unless energy is continually supplied to keep them moving. This conversion from kinetic energy to internal energy is a one-way process – it is impossible to convert directly the internal energy back into kinetic energy of the whole spacecraft.

The internal energy of the spacecraft increases because of the work done by the force caused by air resistance. However, this isn't the only way to increase the internal energy of an object. For example, when you make a cup of tea, you don't boil the water by beating it vigorously with a spoon or whirling the pan very rapidly through the air. A more conventional way of bringing water to its boiling temperature is to place it in contact with an object at a higher temperature, such as the heating element in an electric kettle. The fact that the heating element is at a higher temperature means that the mean kinetic energy of its molecules is greater than the mean kinetic energy of the surrounding water molecules. Collisions between water molecules and molecules of the heating element will, on average, result in water molecules rebounding faster than before and molecules of the heating element moving slower than before. This means that energy is transferred from the heating element to the water. Of course, while the kettle is switched on, electrical energy is continually converted into internal energy in the element, thus maintaining it at a higher temperature than the water. Electrical energy is discussed further in Chapter 7.

This transfer of energy resulting from contact between objects at different temperatures is known as a transfer of heat. In other words:

Heat is energy that flows from a higher temperature object to a lower temperature object because of the temperature difference. When heat is transferred to an object, the internal energy of that object increases.

The word 'heat' is often used to mean internal energy in phrases such as 'the kinetic energy was converted into heat' or 'the heat contained by an object'. However, in a strict scientific sense, heat only refers to the *transfer* of energy caused by a difference in temperature.

6.3   Specific heat capacity – relating heat transfer to temperature change

Temperature is the degree of hotness or coldness of an object, and has been measured in degrees Celsius up to this point in the course. Another unit for measuring temperature is introduced in Section 6.4. Heat is a form of energy and so is measured in joules, but how are heat and internal energy related to temperature? You can begin to answer this question by considering the following situation.

Imagine boiling some water in two pans on a domestic hob or cooker (Figure 6.2). If you were to adjust the controls of the cooker so that energy was supplied to both pans at the same rate, you would expect it to take much longer to boil a full pan of water than to boil a small amount of water in the bottom of the pan (if both amounts had the same temperature initially). In other words, a smaller total amount of chemical or electrical energy is transferred as heat and ultimately converted into internal energy of the water when a small amount of water is boiled than when a larger amount is boiled, even though the final temperature of the water is the same (100 °C) in both cases. Clearly, heat transfer and temperature change are not equivalent.

Figure 6.2   It takes more energy to boil a full pan of water than to boil a small amount of water in an identical pan.

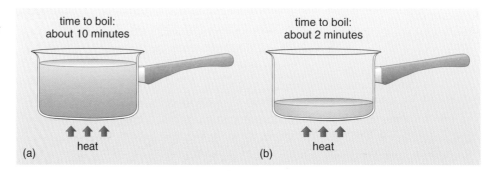

However, there is a connection between these two quantities. Suppose that the pans were now filled with the same amount of water (Figure 6.3), and again heated at the same rate. Obviously it would take longer to heat one panful to 80 °C than it would take to heat the other to 40 °C from the same starting temperature. The higher the temperature to which an object is heated, the more energy that must have been transferred to it, so the greater its internal energy must be.

Figure 6.3   It takes less energy to heat water from room temperature to 40 °C than to heat the same amount of water from room temperature to 80 °C.

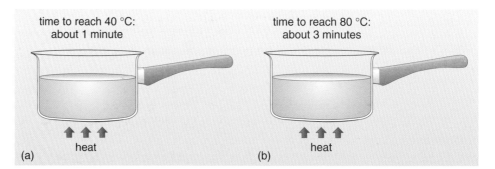

In fact, the temperature rise of an object is proportional to the amount of heat transferred to it. Using the symbol q to represent the heat transferred:

$$q \propto \Delta T \tag{6.1}$$

where ΔT is the change in the temperature.

Figure 6.2 shows that more energy must be transferred to heat a large quantity of water through a particular temperature interval than to heat a smaller quantity of water through the same temperature interval. In fact, in a classic experiment, Joule proved that if the mass of the water were doubled, double the amount of energy had to be transferred to raise its temperature by the same number of degrees, i.e. the heat transfer, q, required to produce a given temperature change in an object is proportional to the mass of that object:

$$q \propto m \tag{6.2}$$

Proportionalities 6.1 and 6.2 can be combined into one:

$$q \propto m \times \Delta T \tag{6.3}$$

As before, this proportionality relationship can be turned into an equation by introducing a constant of proportionality, using the symbol c:

$$q = cm\Delta T \tag{6.4}$$

Since multiplication is commutative (Section 3.3), the terms in Equation 6.4 can be multiplied together in any order, and this equation is usually written as:

$$q = mc\Delta T \tag{6.5}$$

In Equation 6.5, c is known as the **specific heat capacity**, sometimes shortened to 'specific heat'. Note that the symbol c is conventionally used for specific heat capacity as well as for the speed of light. This is unlikely to lead to confusion because the two quantities rarely appear in the same context.

Equation 6.5 can be rearranged to make c the subject (by dividing both sides by m and ΔT):

$$c = \frac{q}{m\Delta T} \tag{6.6}$$

■ What is the appropriate unit of specific heat capacity if heat and mass are expressed in SI units and temperature in °C?

☐ As always, the units on both sides of Equation 6.6 must balance. So

$$\text{unit of } c = \text{unit of } \left(\frac{q}{m\Delta T} \right) = \frac{\text{J}}{\text{kg} \times \text{°C}} = \text{J kg}^{-1}\,\text{°C}^{-1}$$

Equation 6.6 can be expressed in words by saying that the specific heat capacity is the amount of energy that has to be transferred to one unit of mass of material for one unit of temperature increase. Alternatively, the specific heat capacity (in the unit quoted above) is the amount of energy in joules that has to be transferred to 1 kg of material to raise its temperature by 1 °C.

Once again, the 'constant of proportionality' (c in this case) is not universally constant. Different materials have very different values of specific heat capacities, and these values also vary slightly with temperature and pressure. Table 6.1 lists the specific heat capacities of some common materials at a specified temperature and pressure (so-called standard atmospheric pressure). You will note that no value is given for the specific heat capacity of water. This is because you will measure this for yourself in Activity 6.1 at the end of this chapter. Meanwhile, use the information in Table 6.1 to answer Question 6.1. This question acts as a reminder that when you are cooking, heat must be transferred in order to increase the internal energy of the pan as well as its contents.

Table 6.1 Specific heat capacities of some common materials at standard atmospheric pressure and 25 °C.

Substance	Specific heat capacity/J kg^{-1} °C^{-1}
mercury	1.4×10^2
copper	3.8×10^2
glass	8.4×10^2
aluminium	9.0×10^2
air	1.0×10^3
paraffin	2.1×10^3
water	4·2 ~~5.0~~ $\times 10^3$

my result 5·0 × 10³

Question 6.1

(a) How much energy is required to heat a copper pan with a mass of 0.50 kg from 20 °C to 100 °C?

(b) Estimate how much energy would be required to heat (i) a 250 g copper pan and (ii) a 0.50 kg aluminium pan through the same temperature difference as in (a).

6.4 The absolute scale of temperature

Note that the practical work in Activity 6.1 (Section 6.6) may require a small amount of preparation the day before you do the experiment, so you are advised to read the first part of the notes for this activity (up to and including Task 1) now.

The mean kinetic energy of the constituent molecules of an object increases when the temperature of the object increases. It follows that, as an object cools, the mean kinetic energy of the molecules decreases. Eventually a point would be reached at which the molecules have no kinetic energy, and so no further cooling could occur. The temperature at which this would happen is known as **absolute zero**, which is the lowest temperature possible. On the Celsius scale, this temperature has a value of −273.15 °C.

For many scientific purposes, it makes sense to define a temperature scale for which zero on the scale corresponds to this absolute zero of temperature, and on such a scale negative temperatures are impossible. The scale with this property, which is widely used by scientists, is known as the **absolute temperature scale**; it is also known as the Kelvin scale, named after the British physicist and engineer William Thomson, Lord Kelvin (1824–1907). The unit of temperature on this scale is called the **kelvin**, symbol K, and this is the SI unit of temperature. A change of one kelvin is the same as a change of one degree Celsius, so there are 100 kelvin between the normal freezing and boiling temperatures of water. The absolute and Celsius scales are compared in Figure 6.4. To convert degrees Celsius into kelvin, you just add 273.15 to the Celsius temperature. Thus the normal freezing temperature of water (0 °C) is 273.15 kelvin, or 273.15 K.

■ Book 1, Section 4.8 gives the current value of the Earth's GMST as about 15 °C. What is this value in kelvin?

☐ 15 °C is (15 + 273.15) K, or about 288 K. (Note that the absolute temperature is quoted to the nearest kelvin because the Celsius temperature was quoted to that precision.)

The convention for the absolute scale is that the temperature is written without a degree symbol, and so 300 K is said as 'three hundred kelvin' and *not* 'three hundred degrees kelvin'.

This course has stressed the importance of using SI units in calculations, so you may be wondering why degrees Celsius not kelvin have been used until now. The answer is that all the calculations so far have been concerned with changes of temperature; for example, you calculated the energy required to heat a pan through a temperature change of 80 °C. A change of one 1 K is the same as a change of 1 °C, so temperature differences have the same numerical value on both scales. In SI units, the specific heat of copper should be quoted as 3.8×10^2 J kg^{-1} K^{-1} rather than 3.8×10^2 J kg^{-1} °C^{-1}, but the more familiar unit has been used to avoid converting between °C and K all the time. However, there

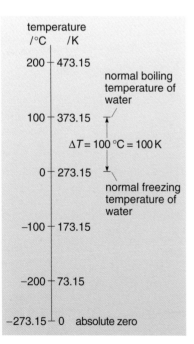

Figure 6.4 A comparison of the Celsius (°C) and absolute (K) temperature scales.

are situations where it is important to use the absolute temperature in calculations and you will meet one such situation in Book 7.

■ Write down an equation for converting temperature in degrees Celsius into temperature in kelvin.

☐ To convert temperature in degrees Celsius into kelvin, you have to add 273.15 to the value of the Celsius temperature, so:

$$\begin{pmatrix} \text{value of} \\ \text{temperature in kelvin} \end{pmatrix} = \begin{pmatrix} \text{value of} \\ \text{temperature in degrees Celsius} \end{pmatrix} + 273.15$$

6.5 Latent heat

Energy must be supplied to raise the temperature of a substance, but energy must also be supplied to change the *state* of a substance. Thus, when you heat water in an electric kettle, its temperature increases until it boils at about 100 °C. At this point, the temperature stops rising, and the energy transferred to the water from the heating element now transforms liquid water into water vapour. You learned in Book 1, Section 4.5.2 that the energy required to change the state of a substance is known as latent heat, where the word latent (meaning 'hidden') reminds you that the change in internal energy that takes place is hidden, in that it does not result directly in a change of temperature. However, the 'hidden' energy difference between a liquid and the same mass of its gas manifests itself in many ways. For example, steam at 100 °C is likely to cause a far more serious scald than water at the same temperature. This is because steam has a greater internal energy.

■ Section 6.1 explained, in molecular terms, why energy has to be supplied to convert a liquid into a gas. Try to recall this explanation without referring back to the earlier section.

☐ You can check your explanation by rereading the penultimate paragraph of Section 6.1.

Now consider how much energy is needed to change a liquid into a gas.

Applying the same reasoning as when discussing specific heat, you can assume that the energy required is proportional to the mass of liquid converted into gas. This can be expressed as:

$$q \propto m \tag{6.7}$$

In this case, the temperature does not change and it does not have to be considered. This simple proportionality relationship can now be converted into an equation in the usual way by introducing a constant of proportionality, which can be called L_v:

$$q = L_v m \tag{6.8}$$

The constant of proportionality L_v is known as the **specific latent heat of vaporisation** and it can be defined as the energy required to vaporise one unit of mass of the liquid at its boiling temperature.

Table 6.2 Specific latent heat of vaporisation of some common materials at standard atmospheric pressure.

Substance	Specific latent heat/J kg^{-1}
oxygen	2.1×10^5
mercury	2.9×10^5
water	2.3 ×10^6
copper	5.2×10^6
aluminium	1.1×10^7

■ What is the SI unit of the specific latent heat of vaporisation?

□ Dividing both sides of Equation 6.8 by m (to make L_v the subject) gives $L_v = \dfrac{q}{m}$. The units of both sides of this equation must be the same, so:

$$\text{unit of } L_v = \text{unit of } \left(\frac{q}{m}\right) = \frac{\text{J}}{\text{kg}} = \text{J kg}^{-1}$$

As with specific heat capacity, the value of the specific latent heat of vaporisation is different for different materials, and varies slightly with pressure. Table 6.2 lists values for some common materials (at standard atmospheric pressure) with boiling temperatures ranging from −183 °C for oxygen to 2567 °C for copper. You can write in the value of the specific latent heat of vaporisation of water after you have completed Activity 6.2.

L_v is known as the specific latent heat of vaporisation but note that, in exactly the same way as energy is required in order for evaporation (vaporisation) to take place, energy is given out when a gas condenses to form a liquid – and all the calculations can be reversed. The specific latent heat of vaporisation is numerically equal to the specific latent heat of condensation.

Latent heat is not only associated with evaporation and condensation. Energy is also required to melt a solid into a liquid, and the reverse of this process – freezing – gives out energy. The heat transferred in this case is given by:

$$q = L_f m \tag{6.9}$$

where L_f is the **specific latent heat of melting** (sometimes called the specific latent heat of fusion), the energy required to melt one unit of mass of the solid. L_f again has units of J kg^{-1}. Note that Equations 6.8 and 6.9 are almost identical but the specific latent heat is different in the two cases. You will determine the specific latent heat of vaporisation of water for yourself in Activity 6.2. The specific latent heat of melting of pure water ice at 0 °C and standard atmospheric pressure is 3.3×10^5 J kg^{-1}. In Question 6.3, at the end of this chapter, you will compare the energy transfers that take place in melting ice to form water, heating the same mass of water from 0 °C to 100 °C and then converting the same mass of water into steam at 100 °C.

Question 6.2

Liquid oxygen boils at −183 °C at standard atmospheric pressure. It can be stored for short periods in a thermos flask, but the heat transferred to the flask from the warmer surroundings causes the liquid oxygen to boil.

(a) What is the boiling temperature of liquid oxygen on the absolute temperature scale?   90.15 K

(b) If 9.5×10^4 J of heat is transferred to the flask in an hour, what mass of liquid oxygen is converted into gas in this period? (Assume that the liquid oxygen is initially at its boiling temperature.)

6.6   Determining the specific heat capacity and the specific latent heat of vaporisation for water

Some scientific experiments require specialised equipment and must be carried out in a laboratory, usually for reasons of safety. However, this is not always the case. In Activity 6.1 you will carry out an experiment, probably in your kitchen, and you will use your results to find a value for the specific heat capacity of water. In doing this, you will develop skills associated with planning an experiment, making and recording measurements and analysing and interpreting results.

Activity 6.1   Measuring the specific heat capacity of water

We expect this activity will take you approximately 1 hour.

Equipment

Electric kettle, marked with power rating (this is usually on the base or side of the kettle, or it may be in the instruction leaflet)

Kitchen scales (if you cannot obtain kitchen scales, the experiment can be adapted so that a measuring jug is used instead)

Watch or clock that indicates seconds

Aim

To determine the specific heat capacity of water.

Introduction

You will determine the specific heat capacity of water by supplying a measured amount of heat, q, to a measured mass, m, of water and recording the resulting temperature rise, ΔT. The specific heat capacity, c, can be determined by using Equation 6.6:

$$c = \frac{q}{m \Delta T} \qquad (6.6)$$

Planning the experiment

Consider how the three quantities on the right of Equation 6.6 can each be measured.

Measuring the heat supplied to the water

The water will be heated in an electric kettle. The kettle should have a label on it indicating its power rating in watts.

■ If the power rating of a kettle is 2.0 kW, how much energy is transferred from the mains electricity supply to the kettle in 20 s?

☐ Power is energy transferred per unit time, $P = \dfrac{E}{t}$ (Equation 4.13), and if you rearrange this equation to make E the subject, you get $E = Pt$. Since 2.0 kW = 2.0 × 10³ W, the energy transferred in 20 s is:

$E = 2.0 \times 10^3 \text{ W} \times 20 \text{ s} = 40 \times 10^3 \text{ J s}^{-1} \times \text{s} = 4 \times 10^4 \text{ J}$

So you can measure the electrical energy supplied to your kettle by simply measuring the time for which it is switched on and multiplying this by the power rating. You will need a watch or clock that indicates seconds to make this measurement. The electrical energy raises the temperature of the heating element, and heat is transferred from the element to the water. You should assume that the heat q transferred is equal to the electrical energy E supplied.

Task 1   Devising ways to measure the mass of water and the temperature rise

You will need to know the mass of the water that you are heating and the temperature rise – and a thermometer is not supplied! Spend a few minutes thinking about how you will determine the mass of water and the initial and final temperatures of the water. The final temperature is straightforward – you should be able to think of a suitable fixed final temperature to which you can heat the water – but determining the initial temperature is a little more difficult.

When you have thought about this, look at the comments on this task at the end of this book before continuing with the activity.

Practical procedure

As discussed in the comments on Task 1, you need to fill your kettle with water *at a known temperature* at the start of the experiment. Depending on how you decide to do this, you may need to make your initial preparations the day before you plan to do the experiment.

Safety Warning

Read the whole of this section before starting the activity and make sure that you have read the section on 'Practical activities' in the *Course Guide*.

When carrying out practical activities, you should always take care to observe the simple safety precautions highlighted in the course book. Very often, as in the case of this activity, these precautions will seem quite obvious and just a matter of using common sense. However that does not mean that you should ignore the safety instructions. The Open University has a duty to give advice on health and safety to students carrying out any activities that are described in the course. Similarly, *you* have a duty to follow the instructions and to carry out the practical activity having regard for your own safety and that of other people around you. Whenever you do practical activities you should think about the hazards involved, and how any risks can be minimised.

Important safety precautions

Take note of the following safety precautions, which apply to all practical activities:

- Keep children and animals away while you are working.
- Clear your working area of clutter. Put all food away. Ensure there is nothing to trip on underfoot.

- Always wash your hands thoroughly after a practical activity.
- Any household items used should be thoroughly cleaned before returning them to domestic use.

In addition, you should note the following precautions specific to this activity:

- Do not attempt to measure the temperature of the hot water. (For the purposes of this activity, you should assume that water boils at 100 °C.)
- You need to be able to observe the water in the kettle in order to identify the point at which it starts to boil. To do this you may need to conduct the experiment with the kettle's lid removed. If so, take extreme care not to be scalded by steam or by boiling water being ejected from the kettle.
- Disconnect the kettle from the mains supply before weighing it.
- Read all the instructions relating to your kettle before use.

More generally:

- Do not touch hot surfaces.
- To protect against fire, electric shock and personal injury, do not immerse cord, plugs or kettle in water or other liquid.
- Do not let the cord hang over the edge of the work surface or touch hot surfaces.
- Disconnect the kettle from the mains supply when filling or pouring.
- Always put in enough water to cover the element; on models with a water level gauge, this is usually indicated by the MIN mark.
- Do not fill above the MAX mark on the water level gauge or inside of the kettle body. If the kettle is overfilled, boiling water may be ejected.
- Ensure that the kettle is used on a firm, flat surface. Do not place the base unit on a metal tray or metal surface while in use.
- Avoid contact with steam from the spout when the water is boiling or just after the kettle has switched off. Take care if opening the lid for refilling when the kettle is hot.
- Extreme caution must be used when moving an appliance containing hot water.
- Always attach a plug to the appliance first, then plug into the wall outlet. To disconnect, turn any control to off, then remove the plug from the wall socket.

Task 2   Obtaining the data

Read through all the instructions for this task before starting the measurements. Note that these instructions assume that you will weigh the water in the kettle; if you are using an alternative method for measuring the mass of water in the kettle, you will have to modify these instructions accordingly.

Disconnect the kettle from the mains cable, empty out any water, and measure the mass of the empty kettle on the kitchen scales. Record this mass in Table 6.3. While the kettle is empty, read the power rating on the label on its base or side, and record this in Table 6.3 too. Note that on some electric kettles, no exact power rating is given. If, for example, your kettle's power is given as 2800–3000 W, you should use the mean value of 2900 W in your calculations. You should use the comments column in the table to record information about the equipment and the procedures you use in the experiment.

Fill the kettle to the 'maximum level' indicator (or to the maximum that your scales will weigh) with water that is at the 'known' initial temperature, measure the mass of the kettle plus water, and enter that value in Table 6.3.

When you are ready to start heating the water, switch on the kettle and simultaneously observe the time to the nearest second. (It will probably be most convenient to switch on the kettle when the seconds indicator passes through zero.) Record the starting time in Table 6.3.

Table 6.3 Results of an experiment to measure the specific heat capacity of water.

Measurement	Result*	Comments
mass of empty kettle	1·117 kg	
mass of kettle + water	2·680 kg	
mass, m, of water in kettle	1·563 kg	± 0·5g.
power rating, P, of kettle	2·0 kW	2000 W (2000 Js⁻¹) 2SF
starting time (power on)	21·12·00	digital watch
finishing time (power off)	21·17·08ᵏᵖ ᵢᵣ	Changed my mind about point at which water was boiling
time interval, t, for heating	5mins 17 secs.	317 Seconds ± 10 sec.
starting temperature	20°C	Stood in jug for 12hrs. ± 2°C
finishing temperature	100°C	± 2°C
temperature change, ΔT	80°C	
electrical energy supplied, $E = P \times t$	6·3 × 10⁵	2000 × 317 Seconds
specific heat capacity of water, $c = \dfrac{q}{m\Delta T}$	5·0 × 10³ Jkg⁻¹ °C⁻¹	$\dfrac{6·3 \times 10^5}{1·563kg \times 80°C}$ $\dfrac{6·3 \times 10^5}{125·04}$

* Make sure that you record the units for each quantity as well as its numerical value.

Observe the water in the kettle. Ignore the small bubbles that are formed on the heating element and on the sides of the kettle but, when the water boils fiercely, switch the power off and simultaneously read the time to the nearest second. Record the switching-off time in the table. If you can't see when the water boils (e.g. if your kettle is filled through the spout and does not have a lid), you may have to use the fact that the kettle switches itself off when the water boils. However, note that in most kettles with an automatic switch-off, the water boils for some time before this is activated, so this method may give less accurate results.

This completes the data collection.

Analysis of results

Task 3   Calculating a value for the specific heat capacity of water

This task can be broken down into four steps.

1   Calculate the mass of water in the kettle, and calculate the time interval for heating, and insert these values in the appropriate rows in Table 6.3.

2   Insert values for the starting and finishing temperatures in the table, if you haven't already done so, and calculate the temperature change.

3   Calculate the electrical energy supplied to the kettle from the power rating P and the time interval t, and write the result in the table.

4   As the electrical energy supplied is equal to the heat, q, transferred to the water, use this value and the values of m and ΔT to calculate a value for the specific heat capacity of water, and write this in the final row of the table.

You should look at the results obtained by a member of the course team before continuing with this activity. These are given in the comments on this activity at the end of this book.

Discussion

You will appreciate that the experiment that you have done has been a little 'rough and ready', but hopefully it has convinced you that you can estimate a quantity such as the specific heat of water using simple equipment and techniques. After all, before making this measurement, you might not have known whether the specific heat capacity of water was 400 J kg^{-1} °C^{-1}, 4000 J kg^{-1} °C^{-1} or 40 000 J kg^{-1} °C^{-1}. You should now spend a few minutes reviewing the experiment. To help you do this, work through Task 4.

Task 4   Uncertainties in the measurements

The idea of uncertainties associated with experimental measurements was introduced in Book 1, Chapter 3. You should now consider what factors might have led to uncertainties in the value that you have obtained for the specific heat of water. In particular, you should note down:

(a)   your estimates of the uncertainties in the measurements of the mass of water used, the temperature difference and the time interval; make a note of these uncertainties in the 'comments' column of the appropriate rows of Table 6.3

(b)   whether all of the electrical energy supplied to the kettle was transformed *Int energy g kelte* into internal energy of the water and, if not, where it went, and what effect *evaporation, latent heat* this had on the measured specific heat capacity *increase the time, increase q, increase C*

(c)   how you could improve on the experiment, using different equipment or a different method, to get a more accurate value for the specific heat capacity.

thermometer lid on

Now look at the comments on Task 4 at the end of this book before continuing with this activity.

Task 5   Writing a conclusion for the experiment

To conclude this activity, write a conclusion for the experiment that summarises the result you obtained, compares it with the accepted value, and indicates the main reasons for the difference between the two values. Try to do this in no more than three sentences.

Now look at the rest of the comments on this activity at the end of this book.

In Activity 6.2 you will calculate a value for the specific latent heat of vaporisation of water. You don't need to do the practical work this time – an account of an experiment carried out by a course team member is provided. If you are asked to write an account of an experiment (e.g. in an assignment question), you should use a similar structure and style to the one used here.

The results of the experiment are also provided in Activity 6.2 but you will need to calculate the final answer.

Activity 6.2   Measuring the specific latent heat of vaporisation of water

We expect this activity will take you approximately 25 minutes.

Below there is an account of an experiment to measure the specific latent heat of vaporisation of water, carried out by a course team member in his kitchen. You should first read the account and the comments after each section, and then tackle the three tasks that follow.

An experiment to measure the specific latent heat of vaporisation of water

> (*Comment*: the title indicates the subject of the experiment.)

Abstract

An experimental measurement of the latent heat of vaporisation of water was carried out using equipment available in the kitchen. The value obtained for the specific latent heat was [......]*. Suggestions are made for ways in which a more accurate value could be obtained.

> (*Comment*: the abstract – sometimes called a 'summary' – summarises in a few sentences what you did and the result you obtained. This allows the reader to assess whether they are interested in reading the account. Although it appears at the beginning, the abstract is often the last part of the account to be written.)

Aim

To determine the specific latent heat of vaporisation of water.

> (*Comment*: the aim states what it is that you are trying to find.)

Introduction

In order to determine the specific latent heat of vaporisation of water (i.e. the energy required to convert one unit of mass of liquid water into vapour), water

---

* On this occasion the final answer has been omitted because you will calculate this in Task 1.

was boiled in an electric kettle for a measured period of time, and the decrease in the mass of water in the kettle due to vaporisation was measured. The energy supplied was calculated from the known power rating of the kettle, and the latent heat was then calculated by dividing the energy supplied by the mass change.

> (*Comment*: the introduction sets out the purpose of the experiment, and how it was carried out, in broad outline. The introduction should be brief – the details are given in the 'Method' section.)

Method

A jug kettle, with a capacity of 2 litres and a power rating of 2.0 kW (marked on a label on the base), was filled about half-full with water from the tap, and heated until the water boiled. It was switched off, disconnected from the mains lead, and the lid removed. Then it was carefully weighed on kitchen scales and the mass of kettle plus water recorded. The scales were the type with a spring under the scale pan; they were graduated in 25 g divisions, and could measure a maximum mass of 5 kg. The kettle was then removed from the scales and reconnected to the mains lead. The power was switched on and simultaneously the time was noted using a digital watch with a seconds display. The kettle was switched off after 4 minutes (to the nearest second) and then reweighed.

Cooling of the kettle and water during the first weighing operation was minimised by carrying this out as quickly as possible; only about half a minute elapsed between switching off the kettle after it had first boiled and switching on again for the 4 minute heating period.

> (*Comment*: the method section describes how you carried out the experiment. You need to include details of the equipment that you used, any special precautions that you took to reduce uncertainties – for example, minimising the time required for the first weighing in this case – and any problems encountered. It is often useful to include a diagram showing how the equipment was set up, or illustrating some detail of the experiment. The length of this section will depend on the complexity of the experiment. If you are writing an account of an experiment in which you have followed a procedure described in some instructions, there is no need to repeat all of the details that are in the instructions – a brief summary is usually enough. Note that scientists generally write their accounts in an impersonal, 'passive' style, such as 'a jug kettle was filled' rather than 'I filled the jug kettle', but this is not essential.)

Results

Table 6.4 Results from an experiment to measure the latent heat of vaporisation of water.

Measurement	Result
power rating of kettle	2.0 kW
initial mass of kettle plus water	1250 g
final mass of kettle plus water	1025 g
mass of water converted into vapour	225g
time power switched on (h:min:s)	10:42:00
time power switched off (h:min:s)	10:46:00
time interval for heating	4.00 mins

69

(*Comment*: the results section is where you present the measurements or observations that you have made. This is often done most neatly using tables and/or graphs, and you should make sure that these are appropriately labelled and the correct units are included. This section should also contain the analysis of the results and the calculation of the final answer, but they are not included here because you will do them in Task 1.)

Task 1   Analysing the results

Complete Table 6.4 by filling in the two blank spaces, and then calculate the energy supplied during the time interval for heating. Use these results to calculate a value for the specific latent heat of vaporisation of water. You should explain and lay out your calculations in a way that would be intelligible to a tutor who was unfamiliar with the experiment.

Task 2   Writing a discussion section

Look again at the account of the experiment, and think back to your experience with the specific heat experiment (Activity 6.1). Note down what you think are likely to be the main sources of uncertainty in measuring the specific latent heat of vaporisation of water in this way. Your notes would form the basis of the discussion section of the report on this experiment.

Task 3   Writing a conclusion

Write a conclusion for the report on this experiment; this needs to state the result clearly but should be no longer than two or three sentences.

Now look at the comments on this activity at the end of this book.

Question 6.3

Use the values that you entered in Tables 6.1 and 6.2 for the specific heat capacity and specific latent heat of vaporisation of water, and a value of $3.3 \times 10^5 \, \text{J kg}^{-1}$ for the specific latent heat of melting of water to find:

(a) the energy required to turn 1.0 kg of ice into water (assume standard atmospheric conditions and that the entire process happens at 0 °C)

(b) the energy required to heat 1.0 kg of water from 0 °C to 100 °C (assume standard atmospheric conditions)

(c) the energy required to turn 1.0 kg of liquid water into steam (assume standard atmospheric conditions and that the entire process happens at 100 °C).

6.7   Summary of Chapter 6

The internal energy of an object is the sum of the kinetic energy associated with random motion of the molecules in the object and the potential energy associated with the forces of attraction between the atoms and molecules. The internal energy can be increased by supplying heat to an object (i.e. by transferring energy by means of a temperature difference) or by doing work on an object (e.g. by forces associated with friction or air resistance).

The heat transferred to an object of mass m and specific heat capacity c to produce temperature change ΔT is $q = mc\Delta T$. The specific heat capacity of a material is equal to the heat transferred to one unit of mass to produce one unit of temperature change: $c = \dfrac{q}{m\Delta T}$.

On the absolute temperature scale, 0 K corresponds to the lowest temperature possible, and is called absolute zero. The temperature in kelvin is found by adding 273.15 to the value of the temperature in °C.

Energy must be supplied to change the state of a substance from a solid to a liquid or from a liquid to a gas. If a gas condenses to form a liquid or a liquid freezes to become a solid, energy is released.

The specific latent heat of vaporisation L_v of a liquid is the energy required to convert one unit of mass of the liquid into vapour without a change in temperature: $L_v = \dfrac{q}{m}$.

The specific latent heat of melting L_f of a solid is the energy required to convert one unit of mass of the solid into a liquid without a change in temperature: $L_f = \dfrac{q}{m}$.

In studying this chapter you have carried out an experiment to determine the specific heat capacity of water and you have been introduced to the style and structure to be used when writing accounts of experimental work.

A written report of an experiment should include a title, an abstract, an introduction, details of the practical procedure you followed (the 'method' section), results (including both your experimental data and the analysis of these data), a discussion of the findings of the experiment (including a consideration of the experimental uncertainties) and a conclusion.

Chapter 7
Electrical energy

In Activity 6.1, you converted electrical energy into internal energy of water in a kettle and, indeed, you probably convert electrical energy into other forms of energy every day of your life. Electricity has revolutionised life all over the world and it is probably true to say that the harnessing of electrical energy is the single most important technological advance of the last 200 years. Not only can it be used to provide light, heat and kinetic energy on a vast scale but also it is the energy source that drives all electronic devices. There are two reasons for the extraordinary utility of electricity. First, electrical energy can be transported over vast distances at little cost; second, and more importantly, it can be transformed into many other forms of energy very easily.

■ Think for a few minutes about the use of electricity in your home. List some of the different forms of energy into which electrical energy is converted.

☐ Your answer might have included some of the following forms of energy:

- light from a light bulb
- infrared radiation from the heating element of a grill or the remote control for a television
- chemical energy in a mobile phone when you recharge its batteries
- sound energy from a radio or television, or from any noisy appliance with moving parts
- kinetic energy of any appliance that has a motor, pump or fan
- internal energy in any appliance that gets hot, such as a cooker, kettle, washing machine or tumble dryer.

To explain the nature of electrical energy, this chapter first introduces some of the basic concepts of electricity, including electric charge, current, voltage and resistance. Then you will see how the amounts of electrical energy associated with various processes can be calculated and measured. You will have an opportunity to update your glossary of symbols and equations and to practise the problem-solving skills introduced in Chapters 4 and 5. In addition, you will discover how proportionality can be represented on a graph, revise the concept of gradient (Book 2, Box 6.1) and meet the equation of a straight-line graph.

7.1   Electric charge

The Ancient Greeks made observations on what are now called 'electrical phenomena' and recorded the fact that when a piece of amber is rubbed with silk it attracts small, light objects. Indeed, the word electricity comes from the Greek word *elektron*, meaning amber. There are many other examples of natural electricity. For example, after vigorously brushing your hair with a plastic hairbrush, you may have noticed that strands of hair are attracted to the brush, particularly if you have fine hair (Figure 7.1).

Figure 7.1   An example of electrical attraction; fine hair is attracted to a hairbrush.

■ Spend a few minutes thinking of other examples of the effects of naturally produced electricity.

☐ You might have thought of crackles (which are the sound produced by small sparks) when clothes made from synthetic fibres are removed on a dry day; balloons sticking to a wall after being rubbed on clothing; and, of course, the most dramatic example of all, lightning. Electricity is also involved in controlling all muscular and nervous activity in the body – including making your heart beat. Even the thoughts you have as you read these words are associated with electrical activity in your brain.

A simple model can be used to explain these and many other phenomena. This was developed from ideas first put forward by the American scientist and statesman Benjamin Franklin (1707–1790). According to this model:

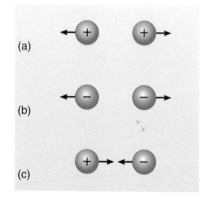

Figure 7.2   (a) Two positive charges repel one another; (b) two negative charges repel one another; (c) a positive charge and a negative charge are attracted towards each other.

• electrical phenomena are caused by a property of matter called **electric charge**, or charge for short

• there are two kinds of electric charge, called positive charge and negative charge

• like charges (i.e. two charges which are both positive or both negative) repel one another; unlike charges (with opposite signs) attract one another (Figure 7.2)

• all matter contains an enormous number of electrically charged particles, with approximately equal numbers of positively charged particles and negatively charged particles. Objects with equal quantities of both types of charge are said to be electrically neutral

• certain actions, such as vigorous rubbing, can transfer charged particles between two initially neutral objects, causing one to become positively charged and the other negatively charged.

This model can be used to explain qualitatively why a hairbrush and hair attract each other (Figure 7.1). The brushing motion causes a transfer of charge between the hair and the brush leaving one positively charged and the other negatively charged. The two unlike charges attract one another, causing the hair to move towards the brush. In the language of science, the unlike charges exert attractive forces on each other. For obvious reasons, the force that occurs between charges is called an **electric force**.

The unit of charge in the SI system is the **coulomb** (pronounced 'koo-lom', symbol C). This is a large unit compared with the amount of electric charge on a hairbrush after brushing hair, which may be about 10^{-8} C. If you had two objects, each with a charge of 1 C, and they were separated by 1 m, the force between them would be about 10^{10} N – that is about 10^4 times greater than the force produced by a jumbo jet's engines during take off!

7.2   Conductors, insulators and semiconductors

Benjamin Franklin's simple model of positive and negative charges can be explained in the light of more recent ideas about atomic structure. You know from Book 1 that all matter consists of atoms, the structure of which is discussed in more detail in Books 4 and 7. For now, simply consider every atom to consist of a tiny nucleus surrounded by a number of even smaller particles called **electrons**. The electrons each carry a negative charge and the nucleus is positively charged. The reason the nucleus and electrons of an atom stay together is precisely the same as the reason hair is attracted to a hairbrush – the electric force pulls them together.

All electrons have the same very small charge: -1.602×10^{-19} C. The charge on the atomic nucleus is equal in magnitude but opposite in sign to the total charge of all the electrons in an atom; thus atoms are electrically neutral overall. Atoms can lose or gain electrons to be left with a net positive or negative charge – the charged atoms are then called ions. Ions are also discussed in more detail in Book 4.

Electrons and ions can move more freely through some substances than they can through others, which leads to some substances being better conductors of electricity than others, that is, they have a higher electrical conductivity. In **electrical conductors**, such as metals and salty water, either electrons or ions can move freely through the substance. In **electrical insulators**, such as rubber, glass and most kinds of plastic, neither electrons nor ions can move freely. The difference between these two types of material is vital for the distribution of electricity and for the operation of electrical appliances in your home (Figure 7.3).

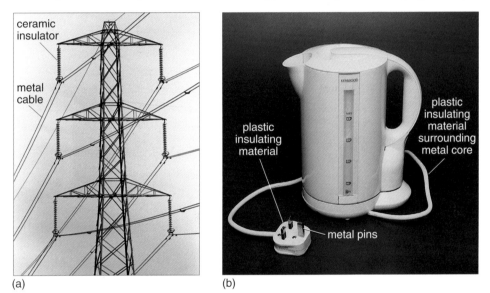

(a)   (b)

Figure 7.3   (a) Electrons can move freely through the metal cables used to distribute electricity but not through the ceramic insulators used to support the cables. (b) Metal pins in the plug and the metal core in the cable conduct electricity to appliances, whilst plastic insulation prevents the electricity from flowing through people (who can be regarded in this context as bags of conducting salty water!)

There is a third class of materials, called **semiconductors**, which are tremendously important as the basis of the electronics and computing industries. Semiconductors have an electrical conductivity which is part way between that of insulators and conductors. However, more importantly, their conductivity can be controlled, so that well-defined regions of a semiconductor material can be made to behave as a conductor while the rest of the material behaves as an electrical insulator. This has led to the development of miniaturised electronic devices on which the electronics and computing industries depend. The properties of semiconductor materials such as silicon are usually enhanced by the introduction of a tiny number of different atoms into an otherwise extremely pure substance, in a process known as 'doping'.

Question 7.1

There are roughly 10^{26} electrons in each kilogram of the human body. Estimate the total negative charge and the total positive charge within your body, in coulombs.

Question 7.2

At the end of Section 7.1, the magnitude of the force between two objects that each have a charge of 1 C and that are separated by 1 m was given as about 10^{10} N. The answer to Question 7.1 showed that the positive charge content of your body and the negative charge content are each far greater than 1 C. In view of this, how can you sit in the same room as another human being (who contains similar amounts of charge) without literally blowing each other away?

7.3   Electric current

In a conducting solid, such as a metal, electrons can move around fairly freely. Therefore, you can picture such a solid as consisting of a 'gas' of negatively charged electrons moving randomly through a fixed array of positively charged ions (Figure 7.4).

Consider what would happen if all the electrons were transferred from one end of a conducting wire to the other. There would then be a large excess of positive charge at the end from which the negatively charged electrons had been removed, and a large excess of negative charge at the other end (Figure 7.5). The electrons, which are free to move, would rush back towards the positively charged end of the wire under the action of the electric force, until their negative charges once again just balanced the positive charges. This flow of negatively charged electrons constitutes what is called an electric current in the wire. In this case, the electric current would stop very quickly, as soon as the electrons had redistributed themselves to cancel out the charge imbalance.

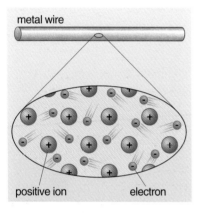

metal wire

positive ion   electron

Figure 7.4   A fixed array of positively charged ions and a 'gas' of negatively charged electrons in an electrically conducting solid. The positive charges on the ions and the negative charges on the electrons balance, so the solid is electrically neutral.

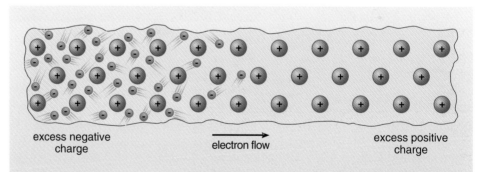

excess negative
charge   electron flow   excess positive
charge

Figure 7.5   Electrons migrating in a conducting wire under the action of electric forces due to the charge imbalance at the ends. The arrow shows the direction of movement of the electrons.

To keep an electric current flowing through the wire, you would need to continually remove electrons from the 'positive end' and replace them at the 'negative end'. In this way a steady state (Book 1, Section 4.2) would be reached, and the electrons would keep travelling along the wire, attracted by the positive charge. This is exactly what an electric battery does. When a conducting wire is connected between the positive and negative terminals of a battery, one end of the wire becomes positively charged and the other becomes negatively charged. The electric force causes electrons to move through the wire towards the positive terminal of the battery, where they are removed from the wire, and at the same time the negative terminal supplies more electrons to the wire. Within the battery there is a net flow of negative charge from the positive terminal to the negative terminal, which balances the flow through the wire, so the charges don't continually build up at the battery terminals (Figure 7.6). The energy required to drive this process comes from chemical reactions within the battery.

When you think about the operation of an electrical device, you don't usually consider the number of electrons, or the quantity of charge, that flows through it. Instead you consider the **electric current** (or current for short), which is defined as the *rate* at which charge flows through the device.

Thus if an electric charge Q passes a given point in a time, t, the electric current, I, is given by:

$$I = \frac{Q}{t} \qquad (7.1)$$

Note that the conventional use of the symbol Q for electric charge is completely unrelated to the use of q to represent heat transferred in Chapter 6.

The SI unit of current is the **ampere** (often shortened to amp, symbol A). A current of one ampere corresponds to a flow of one coulomb of charge per second:

$$1\,A = \frac{1\,C}{1\,s} = 1\,C\,s^{-1} \qquad (7.2)$$

You have probably seen this unit in the specification of electric cables or fuses; a 5 A cable can safely carry a current of 5 A (5 coulombs per second) and a 13 A fuse (Figure 7.7) will blow when the current exceeds 13 A.

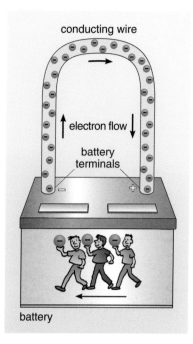

Figure 7.6   A battery can maintain a continuous flow of electrons from its negative terminal to its positive terminal through a conducting wire. At the same time there is a net flow of negative charge within the battery from the positive terminal to the negative terminal. The arrows show the direction of negative charge flow.

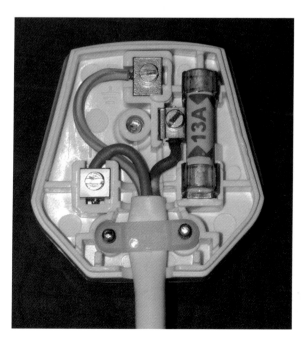

Figure 7.7   An electric plug fitted with a 13 A fuse.

Question 7.3

A current of 5 A flows along an electric cable for 10 minutes. How much electric charge is transferred?

7.4   Electrical energy, volts and electronvolts

When motion under gravity was discussed in Chapter 5, it was useful to think about the situation in terms of changes in gravitational potential energy. Similarly, the motion of electrons in an electric current can be explained by considering changes in their electrical potential energy, which is usually called simply electrical energy.

To see how this works, consider first the flow of water between the two tanks in Figure 7.8a. Tank A is initially filled to a higher level than tank B. If the valve in the pipe is opened, water will flow through the pipe. This is analogous to the flow of electrons through a conductor from the negatively charged end to the positively charged end (Section 7.3). The flow of water in the pipe will slow down and eventually stop when the levels in the tanks equalise, again analogous to the electrical situation. To maintain a steady flow of water in the pipe, water needs to be transported from tank B back to tank A to maintain a difference between the water levels, which can be done with a pump (Figure 7.8b). This is analogous to the action of a battery.

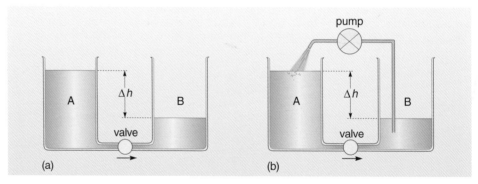

Figure 7.8   (a) If the valve is open, water flows from tank A to tank B until the water levels become equal. (b) A steady flow of water from tank A to tank B can be maintained with a pump to circulate water back from B to A.

Now consider the energy changes in these two situations. When water flows from tank A to tank B, its gravitational potential energy decreases (Section 5.4).

■   What is the decrease in the gravitational potential energy of a mass m of water that falls through a height Δh, as in Figure 7.8?

☐   The decrease in gravitational energy is given by the equation:

$$\Delta E_g = mg\Delta h \tag{5.8}$$

The gravitational energy is initially converted into kinetic energy of the water as it flows through the pipe and into tank B, but some of this kinetic energy is eventually converted into internal energy because of friction between the water and the pipe, so the water gets warmer.

You might have guessed that a similar argument applies to the electrons in the wire – and you would be correct. You can think of electrical energy associated with the electric force in the same way as you think of gravitational energy associated with the gravitational force. When the electrons flow through the wire, their electrical energy decreases, and this energy is initially converted into kinetic energy. However, the moving electrons frequently collide with the positive ions, causing them to vibrate more vigorously and thus transforming some of the kinetic energy of the electrons to internal energy of the wire, which therefore heats up. This 'loss' of electrical energy is the basis of electrical resistance, the subject of the next section.

An equation very similar to Equation 5.8 can be written to describe the change in electrical energy, represented by the symbol ΔE_e. In the gravitational case, the change in gravitational energy is proportional to the mass of the object which moves from one place to another. The change in electrical energy, however, is proportional to the electric charge Q that moves. So:

$$\Delta E_e \propto Q \quad \text{or} \quad \Delta E_e = \text{constant} \times Q$$

This proportionality should seem reasonable; if twice as much charge flows you would expect the change in electrical energy to be twice as great. The constant of proportionality in this relationship is a quantity known as the potential difference or **voltage difference** of the battery, represented by the symbol ΔV. The SI unit of voltage difference is the **volt**, which is abbreviated to V.

Thus the equation for the change in electrical energy when a charge Q moves through a voltage difference ΔV is $\Delta E_e = \Delta V \times Q$ or:

$$\Delta E_e = Q\Delta V \qquad\qquad (7.3)$$

Voltage difference is often referred to simply as 'voltage', which is a term you are probably familiar with. The value of the voltage is given on all batteries and electricity supplies. When someone talks of a 12-volt car battery, they mean that there is a voltage difference of 12 volts between the battery terminals.

Using SI units for each of the three quantities in Equation 7.3, you can see that:

$$1\,\text{J} = 1\,\text{C} \times 1\,\text{V} = 1\,\text{C V} \qquad\qquad (7.4)$$

However, Equation 7.3 is not very often used for electric charges measured in coulombs. People don't often consider the quantity of electric charge flowing through a conductor. It is more usual to think in terms of electric current, measured in amperes, where $1\,\text{A} = 1\,\text{C s}^{-1}$ (Equation 7.2). In Section 7.6, Equation 7.3 will be combined with other equations you have already met to obtain a far more useful equation.

Meanwhile, consider Equation 7.3 in the context of a very much smaller electrical charge; that carried by an electron. Recall that an electron has a negative charge of 1.602×10^{-19} C. Thus, if an electron moves through a voltage difference of one volt, the energy transferred is given by:

$$\Delta E_e = Q\Delta V$$
$$= 1.602 \times 10^{-19}\,\text{C} \times 1\,\text{V}$$
$$= 1.602 \times 10^{-19}\,\text{J}$$

This is a very small amount of energy. However, as you will see when considering the energy associated with light and other radiation and the energies associated with the fundamental building blocks of matter (Book 7), the joule sometimes turns out to be too big a unit to be handled easily. So another unit of energy, the **electronvolt**, is defined as the energy transferred when one electron moves through a voltage difference of one volt. The electronvolt is represented by the symbol eV and:

$$1 \text{eV} = 1.602 \times 10^{-19} \text{ J} \tag{7.5}$$

■ How many electronvolts are there in 1 J?

☐ Since $1 \text{eV} = 1.602 \times 10^{-19}$ J:

$$1 \text{J} = \frac{1}{1.602 \times 10^{-19}} \text{ eV} = 6.242 \times 10^{18} \text{ eV}$$

In the same way as for other units you have met previously, eV can be prefixed with various multiples. So, 1 keV is 10^3 eV, 1 MeV is 10^6 eV and 1 GeV is 10^9 eV.

Remember that the volt is a unit of voltage difference whilst the electronvolt is a unit of energy – don't let the similarity of V and eV lead you to confuse the two units.

7.5   Electrical resistance

In 1827, Georg Simon Ohm, a German schoolteacher and electrician, found that when charge flows through metal wires and some other substances such as graphite, the current flowing, I, is proportional to the voltage difference, ΔV:

$$I \propto \Delta V \tag{7.6}$$

This proportionality, known as **Ohm's law**, can be written the other way round:

$$\Delta V \propto I \tag{7.7}$$

or, using the letter R to represent the constant of proportionality:

$$\Delta V = RI \tag{7.8}$$

R is known as the substance's **electrical resistance**. Equation 7.8 (which is very often written as $V = IR$) can be rearranged (by reversing the equation and dividing both sides by I) to make R the subject

$$R = \frac{\Delta V}{I} \tag{7.9}$$

Note that for many materials, R is not constant. It depends on several factors, including temperature and the current that flows. So Ohm's law (that electric current is proportional to voltage difference) is only true for some materials. However, whether or not R is constant (that is, whether or not Ohm's law is obeyed), a substance's resistance is defined by Equation 7.9. Expressing this in words:

> Electrical resistance is defined as the voltage difference between the two ends of a conductor divided by the electric current flowing through the conductor.

Electrical resistance is a measure of the degree to which an object opposes the passage of electric current. So in superconductors, which are materials in which resistance falls abruptly to zero at low temperatures, current flows unopposed.

At the present time, the huge technological potential of superconductors is limited by the fact that the resistance only drops to zero at extremely low temperatures (typically less than 20 K) and many promising applications have been thwarted by the impracticality of maintaining large devices or lengths of cable at such low temperatures.

Electric circuits use the property of resistance, especially in components known as resistors. The SI unit of resistance is the **ohm**, represented by the Greek capital letter omega, Ω, and resistors are manufactured with values of resistance from around 0.1 to 10^7 ohms.

■ Use Equation 7.9 to express the ohm (Ω) in terms of the volt (V) and the ampere (A).

□ Since voltage difference, ΔV, is measured in volts and current, I, is measured in amperes:

$$1\,\Omega = \frac{1\,\text{V}}{1\,\text{A}} = 1\,\text{V A}^{-1} \tag{7.10}$$

Question 7.4

A torch bulb is connected to a battery which maintains a voltage difference of 1.5 V across the bulb's filament. If the current through the bulb is 0.3 A, what is the resistance of the filament?

7.5.1   Proportionality and straight-line graphs

The proportionality relationship of Ohm's law can be written either as

$$I \propto \Delta V \tag{7.6}$$

or as

$$\Delta V \propto I \tag{7.7}$$

This means that every time the voltage difference is trebled, the current is trebled too, or every time the current is halved, the voltage difference is halved too.

Equations 7.6 and 7.7 can be represented in another way. A graph of I against ΔV (Figure 7.9a) is a straight line going through the origin (i.e. the point where the values of both I and ΔV are zero), as is a graph of ΔV against I (Figure 7.9b).

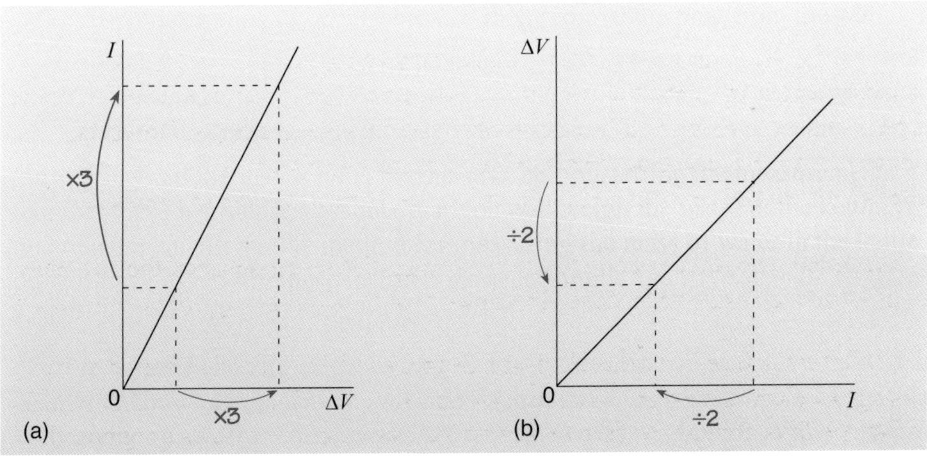

(a)

(b)

Figure 7.9   (a) $I \propto \Delta V$, so a graph of I against ΔV is a straight line going through the origin. Trebling ΔV results in a trebling of I. (b) $\Delta V \propto I$, so a graph of ΔV against I is also a straight line going through the origin. Halving I results in a halving of ΔV.

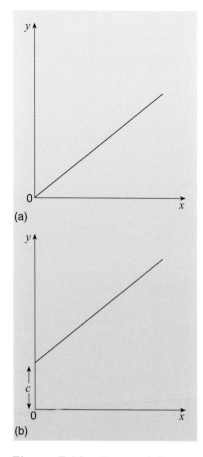

Figure 7.10 Two straight-line graphs. (a) The graph goes through the origin so the quantity y plotted on the vertical axis is directly proportional to the quantity x plotted on the horizontal axis. (b) The graph is a straight line but it does not go through the origin. Instead, when $x = 0$, $y = c$. In this case, y is not proportional to x.

This result is true for all quantities that are directly proportional. So, recalling that the cost of petrol is proportional to the volume bought, if you plotted a graph of the cost of petrol against the volume bought, it would be a straight line going through the origin.

In general:

> If two quantities are directly proportional to each other, a graph plotted of one of the quantities against the other will be a straight line going through the origin.

The converse is also true:

> If a graph plotted of one quantity against another is a straight line going through the origin, the two quantities are directly proportional to each other.

In symbols, if $y \propto x$ then a graph of y against x will be a straight line passing through the origin. If a graph of y against x is a straight line passing through the origin (as in Figure 7.10a) then $y \propto x$.

It is worth emphasising that this result is only true for straight-line graphs that go through the origin so, for the graph in Figure 7.10b, y is not directly proportional to x.

7.5.2   The equation of a straight line

Any proportionality can be converted into an equation by inserting a constant of proportionality, so $y \propto x$ can be written as:

$$y = mx \qquad (7.11)$$

where m is a constant.

Rearranging this equation to make m the subject gives $m = \dfrac{y}{x}$.

Now consider the corresponding graph. This was shown in Figure 7.10a but is redrawn in Figure 7.11.

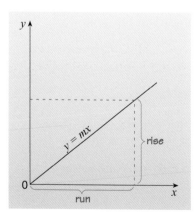

Figure 7.11 For a straight-line graph passing through the origin, the gradient $m = \dfrac{y}{x}$; the equation of the graph is $y = mx$.

■ What is the gradient of a graph?

☐ From Book 2, Box 6.1, gradient $= \dfrac{\text{rise}}{\text{run}}$. However, in this case (since the graph passes through the origin), a run of x corresponds to a rise of y, so:

$$\text{gradient} = \frac{\text{rise}}{\text{run}} = \frac{y}{x}$$

Comparing this with the equation $m = \dfrac{y}{x}$, it is clear that the gradient is m.

So, if $y = mx$, a graph of y against x will be a straight line with a gradient equal to m. Note that when $x = 0$ then $y = 0$, whatever value is taken by m (the gradient of the graph). In other words, when plotted as graphs, equations such as Equation 7.11 always correspond to straight lines that pass through the origin.

■ Equation 7.8 ($\Delta V = RI$) corresponds to the graph shown in Figure 7.9b. What is the gradient of this graph.

☐ The gradient of the graph is $\dfrac{\Delta V}{I} = R$.

Now look at the line plotted on the graph in Figure 7.10b, which is redrawn in Figure 7.12. This has the same gradient as the graph in Figure 7.11, but the whole line has been moved vertically upwards by a distance c. So, for any value of x, you can find the value of y by calculating mx, as for the graph in Figure 7.11, and then adding on an extra amount, c, corresponding to the vertical shift. So the equation that allows a value to be calculated for y from a value of x is:

$$y = mx + c \tag{7.12}$$

This is the general form of the **equation of a straight line**.

From this equation you can see that when $x = 0$, $y = (m \times 0) + c = c$. So the value of c indicates the point at which the line intercepts the vertical axis, often simply referred to as the **intercept**. Such a graph still has a gradient of m, however, as you can see by comparing the gradients of the graphs in Figures 7.11 and 7.12.

■ If c is a negative number, how would the graph differ from that shown in Figure 7.12?

☐ The graph would still be a straight line, and would still slope in the same direction, but it would be shifted downwards so that it intercepted the vertical axis in the region where y is negative.

■ If m is a negative number, how would the graph differ from that shown in Figure 7.12?

☐ The graph would still be a straight line but it would slope *downwards* from left to right.

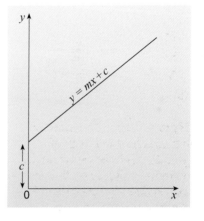

Figure 7.12   Graph corresponding to the equation $y = mx + c$. The graph is a straight line but it does not go through the origin. The gradient of the graph is m and it intercepts the vertical axis at $y = c$.

Comparing equations such as Equations 7.11 or 7.12 with graphs such as Figures 7.11 or 7.12 is a useful way of using the gradient and intercept of a straight-line graph to obtain values for physical quantities. You will use such a method later, in Activity 9.2, to obtain a value for the wavelength of red light. The relationship between Equation 7.12 and Figure 7.12 can be summarised as follows.

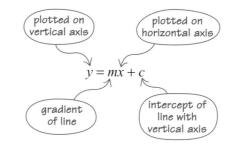

The following example illustrates how this relationship may be used.

Suppose a bus has a constant acceleration, a. The speed of the bus, v, measured at a range of times, t, is given by the equation $v = u + at$, where u is the bus's initial speed. If you plotted a graph of speed, v, on the vertical axis, against time, t, on the horizontal axis, how could you determine the initial speed, u, and the acceleration of the bus, a, from the graph?

The equation $v = u + at$ can be rearranged so that it is similar to Equation 7.12, and each term then has a similar meaning as follows.

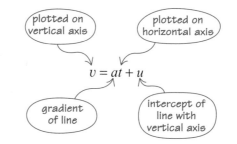

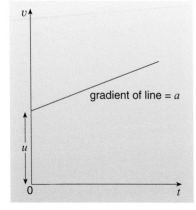

Figure 7.13 A straight-line graph representing the equation $v = u + at$.

So a graph of v against t would have a gradient equal to a and the line would intercept the vertical axis at a point with a value equal to u (Figure 7.13). The acceleration of the bus would therefore be given by the gradient of the graph, and its initial speed (at $t = 0$) would be given by the intercept with the vertical axis.

Question 7.5

Figure 7.14 is a graph showing the variation of voltage difference with electric current for a resistor. What is the electrical resistance of the resistor?

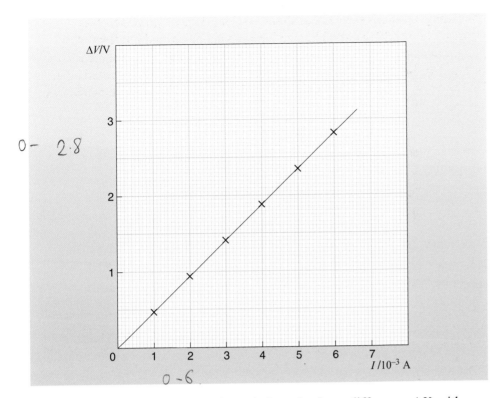

O— 2·8

0 ~6

Figure 7.14 A graph showing the variation of voltage difference, ΔV, with electric current, I, for a resistor.

7.6 Electrical power and more on problem solving

This chapter has introduced many new symbols and equations. In this section they will be used to derive one final equation, this time for electrical power. You will then have an opportunity to update your personal glossary of symbols and equations, before Activity 7.1 invites you to use this glossary and to practise your problem-solving skills.

When an electric current flows through a conductor, electrical energy is continuously converted into other forms of energy, such as internal energy in a heating element, light from the filament of a bulb, or sound from a loudspeaker. In Section 4.3, power was defined as the rate at which energy is converted, and power is another concept that will be familiar to you in the context of electrical appliances. Every electrical appliance in your home should have a power rating which tells you how rapidly the conversion from electrical energy to other forms of energy occurs, but how is the power rating related to current and voltage?

In general, power is given by $P = \dfrac{E}{t}$ (Equation 4.13) where E is the energy converted in time t. For electrical power, E is the change in electrical energy ΔE_e, so Equation 4.13 becomes:

$$P = \frac{\Delta E_e}{t} \tag{7.13}$$

However, electrical energy is given by $\Delta E_e = Q\Delta V$ (Equation 7.3) and substituting $Q\Delta V$ in place of ΔE_e in Equation 7.13 gives:

$$P = \frac{Q\Delta V}{t} \text{ which can be written as } P = \frac{Q}{t} \times \Delta V \tag{7.14}$$

Now, remember that current is defined by $I = \dfrac{Q}{t}$ (Equation 7.1), so $\dfrac{Q}{t}$ in Equation 7.14 can be replaced by I, which gives:

$$P = I\Delta V \tag{7.15}$$

This relationship is very useful. Given any two of the quantities in Equation 7.15, you can calculate the remaining one. For example, suppose that a current of 2.0 A flows through a torch bulb connected to a 6.0 V battery. The power is given by:

$$P = I\Delta V = 2.0 \text{ A} \times 6.0 \text{ V} = 12 \text{ A V} = 12 \text{ W}$$

■ Use the definitions of the amp and the volt to confirm that $1 \text{ A} \times 1 \text{ V} = 1 \text{ W}$.

☐ $1 \text{ A} = 1 \text{ C s}^{-1}$ (Equation 7.2)

  $1 \text{ J} = 1 \text{ C} \times 1 \text{ V}$ (Equation 7.4), so $1 \text{ V} = \dfrac{1 \text{ J}}{1 \text{ C}} = 1 \text{ J C}^{-1}$

  thus $1 \text{ A} \times 1 \text{ V} = (1 \text{ C s}^{-1}) \times (1 \text{ J C}^{-1}) = 1 \text{ J s}^{-1}$ since the C and the C^{-1} cancel. Recall from Section 4.3 that $1 \text{ W} = 1 \text{ J s}^{-1}$, so:

  $1 \text{ A} \times 1 \text{ V} = 1 \text{ W}$

Question 7.6

(a) What is the current flowing through a 20 W car headlamp bulb operating from a 12 V battery?

(b) What charge flows through the bulb in one minute?

Activity 4.1   Keeping track of symbols, units and equations – Part 3

We expect this part of this activity will take you approximately 10 minutes.

This is an appropriate point to check that you have updated your glossary to include the symbols, equations and units from the last few chapters.

There are no comments on this activity.

Activity 7.1   Using your problem-solving strategy

We expect this activity will take you approximately 20 minutes.

Use your problem-solving strategy from Activities 4.2 and 5.1 to tackle the following problem.

Imagine that you are stuck in your car in bad weather, trying to boil water to make yourself a hot drink.

A cup contains 150 g of water at 19 °C. A small heater is immersed in the water and connected to a 12 V car battery. An electric current of 13 A flows through the heating element. Find the time taken to heat all of the water to 100 °C and for one-third of the water to vaporise.

The specific heat capacity of water is 4.2×10^3 J kg^{-1} °C^{-1} and the specific latent heat of vaporisation is 2.3×10^6 J kg^{-1}. When answering the question, assume that the cup is very well insulated, i.e. that all the electrical energy supplied is transferred to internal energy in the water. Will this assumption lead to an answer that is an overestimate or an underestimate of the time taken?

Now look at the comments on this activity at the end of this book.

7.7   Summary of Chapter 7

There are two types of electric charge: positive and negative. Charged objects with the same sign repel each other, whereas those with opposite signs attract each other. An object is neutral if it contains equal amounts of positive and negative charge. The SI unit of charge is the coulomb, C.

Electrons are free to move in an electrical conductor. The flow of electrons constitutes an electric current, which is defined as flow of charge per unit time, $I = \dfrac{Q}{t}$. The SI unit of current is the amp: 1 A = 1 C s^{-1}.

The change in electrical energy when charge Q flows through a voltage difference ΔV is $\Delta E_e = Q\Delta V$. The SI unit of voltage difference is the volt, V.

If a current I flows across a voltage difference ΔV, the electrical resistance of the conductor is defined by $R = \dfrac{\Delta V}{I}$. If current is proportional to voltage difference, R is constant. The SI unit of resistance is the ohm, Ω.

Electrical power is the rate at which electrical energy is converted into other forms of energy: $P = \dfrac{\Delta E_e}{t} = I\Delta V$.

In studying this chapter you have updated your glossary of symbols and equations and practised your problem-solving skills. In addition you have represented proportionality on a graph and been introduced to the equation of a straight line.

If two quantities are directly proportional to each other, a graph plotted of one of the quantities against the other will be a straight line going through the origin. Conversely, if a graph plotted of one quantity against another is a straight line going through the origin, the two quantities are directly proportional to each other.

A straight-line graph with a gradient of m and an intercept on the y-axis of c can be represented by the equation $y = mx + c$.

Chapter 8
Energy from the Sun

This book has described many examples of energy being converted from one form to another – but where does the energy used on Earth come from in the first place? You have considered an archer firing an arrow, a girl bouncing on a trampoline, and various people walking and running. Where do these people get their energy from? The answer, of course, is from the food they eat. The energy content of most pre-packaged food is quoted on the label (e.g. Figure 8.1). Food labels frequently quote energies in both kJ and the non-SI unit kilocalories (kcal), which are sometimes referred to, misleadingly, as Calories (with a capital C). Sticking with SI units, if you consume the snack bar which has the nutritional information given in Figure 8.1, you will gain 536 kJ (i.e. 5.36×10^5 J) of energy.

NUTRITION INFORMATION		
TYPICAL VALUES	PER BAR	PER 100 g
ENERGY	536 kJ 127 kcal	1532 kJ 362 kcal
PROTEIN	1.5 g	4.2 g
CARBOHYDRATE of which sugars	26.3 g 17.2 g	75.0 g 49.0 g
FAT of which saturates	1.8 g 1.1 g	5.0 g 3.2 g
FIBRE	0.6 g	1.8 g
SODIUM	0.1 g	0.3 g
PER BAR 127 CALORIES, 1.8 g FAT, 0.3 g SALT		

Figure 8.1   The nutritional information given on a snack bar.

Going one step further back and asking 'Where does the energy stored in the food come from?', the answer is 'from the Sun'. Plants capture energy from the Sun and use this energy to convert carbon dioxide (from the atmosphere) and water into oxygen and various sugars (such as glucose). This process, known as photosynthesis, is part of the carbon cycle (Book 1, Chapter 7) and is discussed in more detail in Book 5. All you need to remember for now is that part of the energy absorbed from the Sun is stored in the sugars as chemical energy. Eventually, the sugar molecules are broken down into other molecules in another process, called respiration, which is also discussed in more detail in Book 5. Respiration takes place in plants, in the animals (including humans) that eat the plants and in the animals (including humans) that eat the animals who have eaten the plants … and so on. The chemical energy stored in the sugars is then released, and this enables other processes to take place within all living organisms. So, in a very real sense, the Sun is the source of all life on Earth.

8.1   Uses of solar energy

As well as being the energy source for almost all life on Earth, solar energy can also be harnessed in several ways, both directly and indirectly, for a wide variety of uses.

Many devices exist that convert solar radiation directly into other forms of energy. For example, solar collectors for domestic water heating are now commonplace (Figure 8.2a), and Figure 8.2b shows how such a typical solar collector works. The incoming solar radiation is absorbed by the black metal plate, raising its temperature and the temperature of water in pipes attached to the plate. The heated water circulates from the collector to the hot-water tank in the house, where it transfers energy to the water stored in the tank, and then returns to the collector to be reheated.

Figure 8.2   (a) A solar collector on a house. (b) The operation of a typical solar collector.

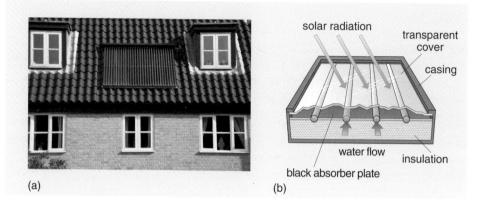

The solar collectors shown in Figure 8.2 convert solar energy directly into internal energy. In contrast, solar cells (also called photovoltaic cells) convert solar energy into electrical energy. Solar cells are used to provide electrical power for a wide range of applications, from hand-held calculators (Figure 8.3a) to the instruments on Earth-orbiting satellites and the robotic rovers used to explore the surface of other planets (Figure 8.3b). Solar cells are particularly useful in remote locations where there is plenty of sunshine but no mains electricity (Figure 8.3c); the solar cells used in outer space are in a particularly remote location!

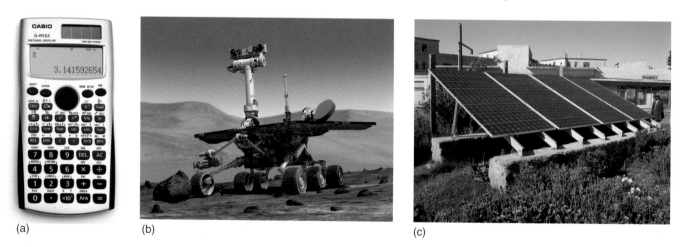

Figure 8.3   The use of solar cells to provide electrical energy: (a) for a scientific calculator; (b) on the Mars rovers 'Spirit' and 'Opportunity', which landed on the planet in January 2004 and were still going strong when this book was printed in late 2007; (c) at a location in Africa.

Indirect use of solar energy occurs every time a piece of wood is burned. When a tree is alive, it absorbs solar energy through its leaves and converts this energy into chemical energy, in the process of photosynthesis described above. Some of the chemical energy is stored in the tree. When a piece of wood is burned, the stored chemical energy is released, and is transferred to the surroundings in the form of heat and light, so that ultimately the internal energy in the immediate surroundings increases. The same is true of coal, natural gas, oil and oil-derived products, such as petrol. All were formed from the remains of life forms that existed hundreds of millions of years ago. The next time you drive a car, or use electrical energy from a coal-fired power station, it is worth reflecting that you are using energy that originally came from the Sun long before humans existed on the Earth.

As well as being the energy source for all of these fuels, solar energy is indirectly responsible for several of the 'renewable' energy sources.

■   Why can wind energy be thought of as a form of solar energy?

☐   The winds on the Earth's surface are caused by the uneven heating of the atmosphere and it is solar energy that provides the atmosphere's internal energy in the first place.

Wave power and hydroelectric power also come indirectly from the Sun. Waves are generated by the wind, which in turn is generated by solar energy. In addition, solar energy is the source of the energy required for the water cycle (Book 1, Chapter 6), and hydroelectricity can be generated when water flows downhill through water turbines.

8.2   Nuclear fusion – energy from the heart of the Sun

Section 8.1 followed the energy trail back to the Sun, which is the source of much of the energy that is available on the Earth. If you take the next logical step and ask where solar energy comes from, the answer is that the Sun is a vast nuclear power station, and the ultimate source of solar energy comes from the nuclear reactions in the Sun itself (Figure 8.4a). The phrase 'nuclear reactions' refers to changes that happen within the tiny nuclei of atoms (nuclei is the plural of nucleus).

(a)   (b)

Figure 8.4   Two 'nuclear power stations'. (a) The Sun has a power output of about 4×10^{26} W and is fuelled by hydrogen in its core. (b) In comparison, the 1.2×10^9 W (1200 MW) of electrical power generated by the uranium-fuelled Sizewell B power station on the Suffolk coast is tiny. It would require 3×10^{17} such power stations to match the Sun's power output.

lifetime = once 1.335×10^{30} kg used

2.12×10^{18} s

3.53×10^{16} min

5.89×10^{14} hr

2.45×10^{13} day

6.7×10^{10} y^{-1}

6.7×10^{4} Ma

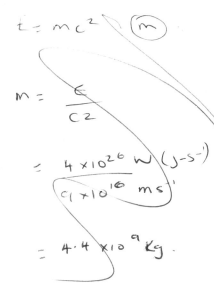

$t = mc^2$ (m)

$m = \dfrac{E}{c^2}$

$= \dfrac{4 \times 10^{26} \, W \, (J\,s^{-1})}{(9 \times 10^{16} \, m \, s)}$

$= 4.4 \times 10^{9}$ kg.

The nuclear reaction that occurs within the Sun's core is, as you learned in Book 2, Section 12.2, called **nuclear fusion**. The name 'fusion' relates to the fact that two atomic nuclei are fused together to make a larger nucleus; in the case of the Sun, hydrogen (the principal constituent of the Sun) is converted into helium. The nuclear power stations constructed on the Earth depend on a different sort of nuclear reaction, called **nuclear fission**, in which an unstable atomic nucleus splits into two roughly equal halves. Nuclear fusion and nuclear fission are discussed in more detail in Book 7 but, for now, note that in both processes the total mass of the products of the reaction (mainly helium in the case of the Sun) is less than the total mass of the initial nuclei (of hydrogen in the case of the Sun). Mass seems to disappear, yet vast quantities of energy are produced, seemingly from nowhere.

The key to understanding what is going on in the Sun, and in other nuclear reactions, lies in Einstein's famous equation:

$$E = mc^2 \tag{8.1}$$

According to Einstein's theory of relativity, energy and mass are not distinct quantities. Energy can be transformed into mass, and mass can be transformed into energy, just as kinetic energy can be transformed into gravitational potential energy, and vice versa. Thus mass is equivalent to energy. Equation 8.1 tells us the conversion factor from mass to energy: the amount of energy E that is contained in mass m is mc^2 where c is the speed of light (3.0×10^8 m s^{-1} to two significant figures). This is a difficult concept to grasp, so let's look at some consequences to clarify exactly what it means.

■ According to Einstein's equation, how much energy is contained in 1 kg of matter?

☐ $E = mc^2$

$= 1 \, \text{kg} \times (3.0 \times 10^8 \, \text{m s}^{-1})^2$

$= 9 \times 10^{16} \, \text{kg m}^2 \, \text{s}^{-2}$

$= 9 \times 10^{16} \, \text{J}$

This is a huge amount of energy. It is equivalent to the energy produced by a 300 MW power station operating for about 10 years; alternatively, it is enough to keep a 100 W light bulb operating for about 30 million years! So a small amount of matter is equivalent to a very large amount of energy. It is the release of some of the energy that is stored in matter that is responsible for the large outputs of energy from fusion reactions in the Sun and from the nuclear reactions in a nuclear power station. The same conversion of matter into energy, occurring in an uncontrolled fashion, is responsible for devastating nuclear weapons of war.

Activity 8.1 gives you an opportunity to investigate the conversion of mass to energy in the Sun.

$6 \cdot 3 \times 10^{11} \, \text{kg s}^{-1}$

0.7%

Activity 8.1   The Sun's source of energy

We expect this activity will take you approximately 20 minutes.

(a) When hydrogen is converted into helium in the core of the Sun, about 0.7% of the mass of hydrogen is converted into energy. How much energy is produced from 1 kg of hydrogen? $6 \cdot 3 \times 10^{14} \, \text{J}$

(b) The power output from the Sun is 4×10^{26} W. What mass of hydrogen must be converted into helium *each second* to produce this power?

(c) The Sun's mass is 2×10^{30} kg, and initially 75% of this was hydrogen (and most of the rest was helium). The rate at which hydrogen is converted into helium remains roughly constant throughout the Sun's life, and the Sun will reach the end of its life in its present form when the hydrogen in the hot central core – 15% of the hydrogen initially in the Sun – has been converted into helium. Use this information to calculate the Sun's lifetime.

Now look at the comments on this activity at the end of this book.

[handwritten notes in right margin:]
$0.007 \, \text{J kg}^{-}$

$1 \text{W} = 1 \text{J s}^{-1}$

75% Hydrogen 1.5×10^{30}
25% Helium 5×10^{29}
2×10^{30} kg mass.

$\boxed{11\% \text{ Hydrogen} \\ 1.65 \times 10^{29} \text{Kg}}$

The mass of hydrogen converted each second, which you calculated in Activity 8.1, may seem inconceivably large. However, if you compare it with the mass of the Sun, which is 2×10^{30} kg, it is very small, which is why the Sun has a very long lifetime. Astrophysicists estimate that the Sun has been shining for about 5×10^9 years, and has enough hydrogen left in the hot core to continue shining for about another 5×10^9 years. This adds up to 10^{10} years between birth and death, which is the value you calculated in Activity 8.1. You will return to this topic in Book 7. The rest of Book 3 considers the means by which the Sun's energy travels to the Earth. We start by considering the energy transferred as visible light.

8.3   What is light?

Optics, the study of light, is a very old science. It was Isaac Newton who first showed that when a beam of light from the Sun is passed through a glass prism it is broken up into a range of colours similar to a miniature rainbow (Figure 8.5). Such a band of colours is called a **spectrum** (plural spectra) and you will investigate the spectra from several sources later in this book.

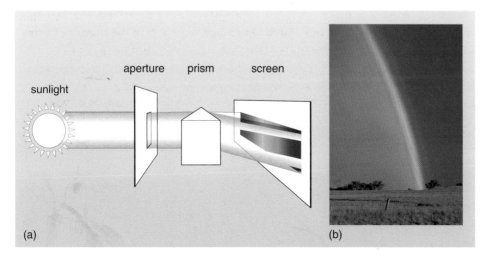

(a)   (b)

Figure 8.5   (a) When a narrow beam of white light from the Sun is passed through a prism, a spectrum of different colours can be observed on a screen. In Chapter 11 you will observe similar spectra for yourself but using a device called a diffraction grating rather than a prism to separate the light into its different colours. (b) A naturally occurring spectrum – a rainbow. Here the light from the Sun is dispersed by passing through raindrops.

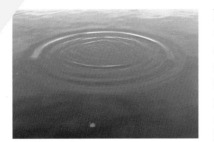

Figure 8.6   A stone dropped into the centre of a pond generates waves on the surface of the water.

Newton, who first observed a spectrum in 1666 and published his *Treatise on Opticks* in 1704, considered light to be made up of tiny particles, or 'corpuscles' of different colours. However, a contemporary of Newton's, the Dutch scientist Christiaan Huygens (1629–1695) proposed another explanation, namely that light is a wave phenomenon. You considered seismic waves in Book 2, Section 3.4.2 and, in general, a **wave** may be defined as a periodic, or regularly repeating, disturbance that transports energy from one place to another. A stone dropped into the centre of a pond generates waves on the surface of the water (Figure 8.6). These waves travel outwards and the energy they transport would eventually cause a cork at the edge of the pond to bob up and down with a regular motion.

Many of the properties of light, including the property of diffraction which is discussed in Chapter 9, can be explained extremely well by Huygens' wave model of light. Furthermore, as a result of the work of one of the greatest physicists of the 19th century, James Clerk Maxwell (1831–1879), light was known to be an electromagnetic wave, an important component of Maxwell's theory of electromagnetism. (This theory links the laws of electricity and magnetism and will be discussed in Book 7.) The passage of light (also called its propagation), from the source that emits it to the detector that absorbs it, is beautifully accounted for using the ideas of waves. However, at the beginning of the 20th century, physicists – notably Albert Einstein (1879–1955) – realised that there were some phenomena for which the wave model seemed incapable of providing a satisfactory explanation. These are phenomena that involve the interaction of light with matter, and they include the photoelectric effect, which is the subject of Chapter 10.

Einstein proposed that light of any specific colour consists of identical *particles*, each with a particular energy depending on the colour of the light. These particles of light are now called **photons** and the amount of energy carried by a single photon is called a **quantum** (plural: quanta). You will return to the subject of quantum physics in Book 7, and the reason for the name will become more apparent then. The question for now is: does the idea of photons of light interacting with matter mean that there is something seriously wrong with the electromagnetic wave description? The short answer to this question is no. Physicists and engineers can largely forget about the particle model of light when predicting how it will pass through lenses and prisms, or the diffraction grating that you will use in Chapter 11. If you ask what light is like, the answer depends crucially on the type of question. If you ask about light travelling from place to place (propagation), the answer is wave-like. If you ask about light interacting with matter, for example being created or detected, the answer is particle-like.

So what is light really like? Book 1 Section 4.2.1 introduced the idea of a model as a simplified description of something in the real world. To explain the behaviour of light, *two* models are used and which model applies at any time depends on the situation.

Light propagates like a wave and interacts like a particle.

For some people this is disturbing. Why can't light make up its mind? For other people, it is rather comforting that two ideas, derived from the macroscopic world of things such as waves on water and bullets hitting targets, should both help to explain something that is so vital to our wellbeing and to our understanding of the natural world. The rest of this book will help you to see how this **wave–particle duality**, while seeming a rather weird idea at first, can provide an excellent explanation for all of the phenomena associated with light. First we consider the Sun's spectrum in more detail and think about the energies of the photons of the different colours it contains.

8.4   Colour and spectra

The spectrum shown in Figure 8.7a comprises an uninterrupted band of colours so it is called a **continuous spectrum**. Thus so-called 'white light' (e.g. from the Sun or a tungsten filament light bulb) actually comprises a range of colours, and colour is a property of light itself. There is colour all around us – green leaves, blue skies, multicoloured plants and animals, and so on. But why do things have colour? Why is the petal of one flower yellow, while another appears blue? The answer lies ultimately in the way light interacts with atoms in the petals, leaves and sky, etc.

It is not the case that atoms themselves are coloured but, rather, that atoms and molecules absorb and emit light. Furthermore, each of the hundred or so different kinds of atom shows a preference for absorbing or emitting light of certain specific colours. Thus, just as every human being has their own set of characteristic fingerprints, so every type of atom (or each chemical element if you prefer, since a chemical element is a substance that consists of just one type of atom) has its own associated pattern of colours of light that it can absorb or emit – a sort of colour-coded fingerprint.

■ Why does a leaf appear green when illuminated by white light?

☐ The atoms and molecules of which the leaf is made absorb all the colours that comprise white light *except* for the green light. Some of the green light passes through the leaf, but most is reflected back from its surface, making the leaf appear green to the human eye.

This association between colour and chemical composition is evident from everyday life. For instance, you are probably familiar with the yellow glow produced by sodium street lights when an electric current passes through vaporised sodium, and you may be familiar with the bright orange-red light of a neon sign. Such associations are even more apparent when a glass prism is used, in an arrangement similar to that in Figure 8.5a, to disperse the light from a source of known chemical composition.

If you did this using a beam of light from a yellow sodium lamp, the resulting spectrum would include lines of several colours (Figure 8.7b), with what appears to be a dominant yellow line (it is actually two bright lines very close together). The lines in the spectrum are called **spectral lines** and, since the light that is responsible for the lines is emitted by sodium atoms, they are known as **emission lines** and the whole spectrum is called the **emission spectrum** of sodium.

Figure 8.7 (a) A continuous spectrum from a beam of white light. (b) The emission spectrum of sodium. Note that this illustrates only the visible spectrum; sodium atoms also emit radiation that is not visible (e.g. infrared and ultraviolet radiation). (c) The visible part of the absorption spectrum of sodium.

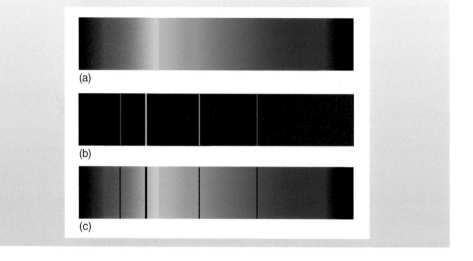

So the association between sodium and the precise shade of yellow light that characterises it can be determined by examining the light emitted by sodium atoms. Exactly the same association may be seen by observing how white light is absorbed by sodium atoms. This is done by passing a beam of white light through sodium vapour (Figure 8.8) and examining the spectrum of the emerging beam to see whether any colours are missing. Figure 8.7c shows the resulting **absorption spectrum** of sodium; as you can see, it exhibits dark **absorption lines**, marking the absence (due to absorption by the sodium vapour) of exactly the same colours that were seen in the emission spectrum (Figure 8.7b).

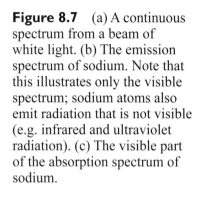

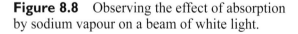

Figure 8.8 Observing the effect of absorption by sodium vapour on a beam of white light.

Sodium atoms are by no means unique in having a characteristic pattern of spectral lines. In fact, every kind of atom has an associated, characteristic 'spectral fingerprint'. Figure 8.9 shows the visible emission spectra of a few common chemical elements. In each case the light being examined originates from a lamp that contains a huge number of atoms of the relevant type, and the observed spectrum is characteristic of every atom of that type. For this reason, the kind of emission spectra shown in Figure 8.9 are often called **atomic spectra**. For obvious reasons, spectra of the types shown in Figures 8.7b, 8.7c and 8.9 are also called **line spectra**.

The fact that atoms have spectral fingerprints of the kind shown in Figure 8.9 has proved extremely useful to scientists. Long before the origin of such atomic spectra had been explained, scientists were using them to identify the chemical composition of vapours and flames. The basic idea is that if you observe the

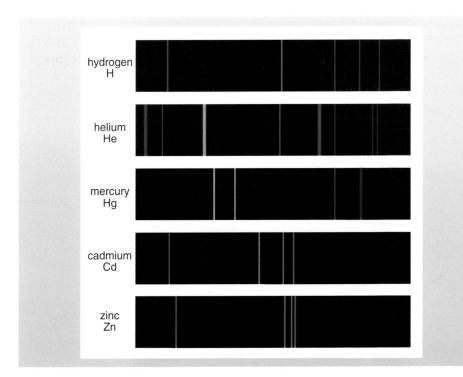

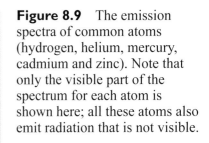

Figure 8.9   The emission spectra of common atoms (hydrogen, helium, mercury, cadmium and zinc). Note that only the visible part of the spectrum for each atom is shown here; all these atoms also emit radiation that is not visible.

spectral fingerprint of an atom in a situation, you can be sure that the atom is present, much as a criminal investigator uses fingerprints left at the scene of a crime to decide whether a suspect was present when the deed was done.

Question 8.1

White light is passed through a vapour of unknown composition. The absorption spectrum of the light that emerges from the vapour is shown in Figure 8.10. By comparing Figure 8.10 with Figure 8.9, identify the unknown vapour.

Hydrogen

Figure 8.10   The absorption spectrum of the unknown vapour in Question 8.1.

This technique is particularly useful for scientists who are observing matter at a great distance in stars and galaxies. For example, the visible spectrum of the Sun is not a simple continuous spectrum; careful examination reveals a series of dark lines (Figure 8.11). The dark lines are called Fraunhofer lines after their discovery by the German optician Josef von Fraunhofer in 1814, and they are characteristic of an absorption spectrum, created as the light has passed through

Figure 8.11   The Sun's visible spectrum.

certain gases in the Sun's outer layers. In 1868, the English astronomer Norman Lockyer observed a previously unknown absorption line in the spectrum of sunlight. He suggested that this evidence pointed to the existence of an element that had not been detected on Earth and which he named helium (after the Greek *helios*, meaning Sun). It was another 27 years before helium was detected on Earth.

8.5   The energies and intensities of light

What is the energy of a photon of light? The answer depends on the colour of the light – in terms of the colours of the rainbow, photons of red light have the lowest energy, whereas those of violet light have the highest energy. This link between colour and energy may be appreciated from Figure 8.12. The colour of the light emitted by a hot object shifts from red to orange to yellow as the temperature increases. Recall from Section 6.2 that temperature is a measure of the internal energy of an object. So, as you increase the temperature of an object, its internal energy increases. As a result, the energy of the typical photons that the object emits also increases, corresponding to a shift in colour from red to yellow, for instance.

Figure 8.12   The light emitted by a hot glowing ball changes colour from red to orange to yellow as the temperature of the ball is increased from (a) to (d).

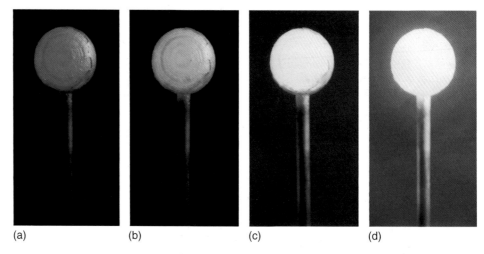

(a)   (b)   (c)   (d)

Light of just one colour is said to be **monochromatic**, from the Greek words *mono*, meaning single, and *chroma*, meaning colour. Monochromatic light consists of identical photons that each have exactly the same energy, determined by the colour of the light. It is quite straightforward to calculate the energy of each photon of light, but that calculation is left until Chapter 10; for now the results are stated. The value of the energy, in joules, corresponding to photons of each colour of the rainbow is indicated by the energy scale under the continuous spectrum in Figure 8.13. You can see that the energies corresponding to the visible part of the spectrum are characterised by rather cumbersome numbers when expressed in joules, so units of electronvolts are used instead (see Section 7.4). One electronvolt (eV) is equal to about 1.6×10^{-19} J.

Question 8.2

Photons of green light have an energy of about 3.8×10^{-19} J. What is the value of this energy when expressed in terms of electronvolts rather than joules?

2·4 eV

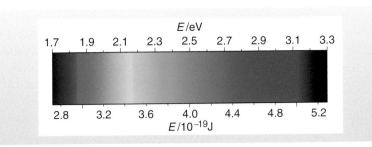

Figure 8.13   The continuous spectrum of visible radiation. The photon energies corresponding to different colours can be determined using the energy scales shown above (in electronvolts) and below (in joules) the spectrum.

As Question 8.2 shows, the electronvolt is a very convenient unit because it reduces the need to use cumbersome powers of ten notation when discussing the energies of photons of light. Photons of visible light have energies ranging from just under 2 eV to just over 3 eV.

Up to now, all spectra have been represented pictorially in the manner of the top half of Figures 8.14a and b. However, to illustrate things more quantitatively, we need a method of plotting a spectrum as a graph. The equivalent graphs of these spectra are shown in the bottom halves of Figure 8.14. Photon energy, E_{ph}, is plotted on the horizontal axis. For the vertical axis, it is conventional to plot a quantity called **intensity**, which is the power per unit area that is carried by the light in a small range of photon energies centred on E_{ph}. Intensity is related to the *number* of photons of a particular energy that are present. A plot of the intensity against the photon energy (such as in the bottom halves of Figure 8.14) is called a **spectral distribution**. It shows, quantitatively, how the energy carried by the light is distributed between different parts of the spectrum. You can think of a spectral distribution as representing how dark or bright a spectrum appears at a given energy; the brighter the spectrum, the more intense the light registered in the spectral distribution at that energy.

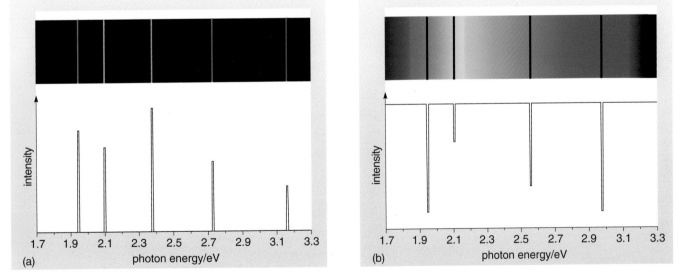

Figure 8.14   Examples of (a) an emission spectrum and (b) an absorption spectrum. The top half represents spectra in the energy range corresponding to visible light. The bottom half shows these same spectra, but converted into graphs of intensity against photon energy, called spectral distributions. The two ways of representing a particular emission spectrum or absorption spectrum are entirely equivalent to each other. However, the spectral distributions are more quantitative, since they show not only where the emission lines and absorption lines occur but also how intense the light is in each part of the spectrum.

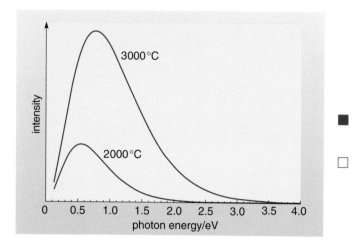

Figure 8.15   Continuous spectral distributions of radiation emitted from a heated metal at temperatures of 2000 °C and 3000 °C.

Continuous spectra can also be represented as graphs (Figure 8.15). These spectral distributions are produced by a metal that is heated to the temperatures shown. The 'glowing balls' in Figure 8.12 emit continuous spectra with similar spectral distributions to these.

■ At what photon energy does the peak intensity occur for each spectrum in Figure 8.15?

☐ The peak intensity of the spectrum emitted by a metal at 2000 °C occurs at about 0.5 eV. The peak intensity of the spectrum emitted by a metal at 3000 °C occurs at about 0.8 eV.

Since the peak intensities of these spectra occur at energies of less than 2 eV, most of the radiation emitted is not in the form of visible light. Heated metals emit most of their radiation in the infrared part of the spectrum. However, heated metals do emit some visible light (with photon energies between 2 eV and 3 eV). This is why a tungsten filament light bulb (whose filament reaches a temperature of about 2500 °C) produces some visible light. Note though that most of the radiation produced by a light bulb of this type is 'wasted' since it emerges in the infrared part of the spectrum. This means that tungsten filament light bulbs consume considerably more energy than is useful in producing light, a factor that eventually led several countries to decide to phase them out. In Chapter 11 you will investigate the properties of 'energy-saving' light bulbs and see why they are so named.

Many objects produce continuous spectra whose distributions have similar shapes to those shown in Figure 8.15. These spectral distributions depend *only* on the temperature of the object, not its composition. The important point to note about such spectra is that at higher temperatures, the peak intensity occurs at higher energies. The surface of the Sun has a temperature of about 5500 °C, and its spectrum has a similar shape to those in Figure 8.15. However, the peak intensity of the Sun's spectrum occurs at higher energies – towards the visible part of the spectrum – simply because the Sun is hotter. In contrast, the peak intensity of the Earth's spectrum is in the infrared region, which explains the importance of infrared radiation when you considered energy transfers in the Earth's atmosphere in Book 1.

Question 8.3

Using information from Sections 8.4 and 8.5, make rough sketches of the spectral distributions corresponding to:

(a) light from a sodium street lamp

(b) light from a tungsten filament light bulb, after it has passed through sodium vapour.

0·6 eV @ 2000°C

0·8 eV @ 3000°C

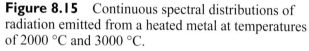

8.6   Beyond light

The human eye is sensitive to light that comprises the familiar rainbow of colours but these are only a small part of the vast **electromagnetic spectrum**. Photons of **infrared radiation** (discussed in Section 8.5 and in Book 1, Section 4.3) have energies less than those of visible light whereas photons of **ultraviolet radiation** have energies greater than those of visible light. This is easy to remember if you note that infra is Latin for below and ultra is Latin for beyond, so infrared (IR) radiation is 'below red' whilst ultraviolet (UV) radiation is 'beyond violet'.

In his *Treatise on Electricity and Magnetism* published in 1873, James Clerk Maxwell predicted the existence of **electromagnetic radiation** beyond the infrared and ultraviolet regions of the spectrum but, unfortunately, he didn't live to see his prediction verified when the German physicist Heinrich Hertz produced radio waves in 1888. Figure 8.16 shows the photon energies of all types of radiation in the electromagnetic spectrum. As you can see, the range of photon energies is huge; for example, the X-ray photons used in radiography have at least a thousand times the energy of photons of light. Note that, although names have been assigned to different regions of the electromagnetic spectrum (e.g. X-rays and infrared), the spectrum is continuous, and there is some overlap between the different regions.

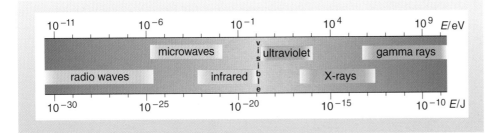

Figure 8.16   The electromagnetic spectrum with photon energy scales in joules and electronvolts. Note that the range of photon energies is so large that a powers of ten scale has been used; the energy changes by a factor of ten for each division along the scale.

All types of electromagnetic radiation share the properties of light that are discussed in Chapters 9, 10 and 11. However, the fact that they have different photon energies leads to different types of electromagnetic radiation being used for a wide range of purposes. Radio waves are at the low-energy end of the electromagnetic spectrum and are so named because they are used to carry radio and television signals. Radio waves are not readily absorbed by most sorts of matter, and they can travel great distances through space; this is why they have been used successfully in radio astronomy to make some remarkable observations, including the discovery of pulsars – tiny collapsed stars rotating at up to several hundred times a second and emitting intense beams of radio waves. Microwave photons have a higher energy than radio waves, although the transition between microwaves and radio waves is not well defined. In addition to their use for cooking, microwaves, like radio waves, are used in communications. Mobile phones operate in the microwave range of the electromagnetic spectrum (Figure 8.17a).

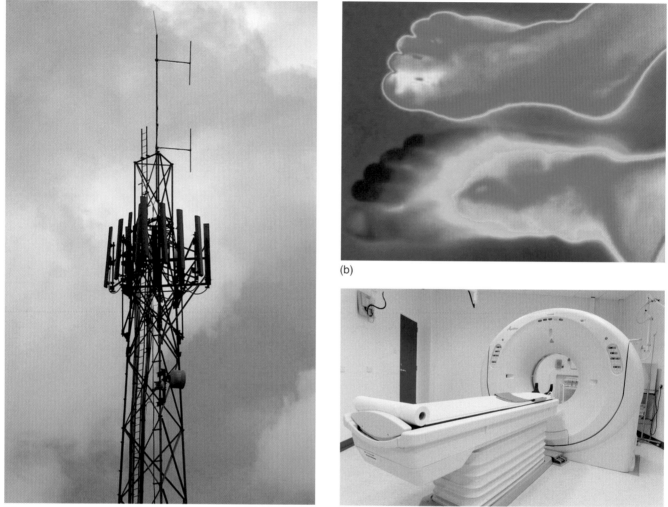

(a)

(b)

(c)

Figure 8.17   Some uses of electromagnetic radiation. (a) An antenna used as part of the UK mobile phone network which relies on microwave signals. (b) An infrared image indicates poor circulation in a human foot (the lower image) compared to a foot with normal circulation. The temperature range goes from hot (white) to cold (blue). (c) A modern CT scanner, which uses X-rays to build up a detailed three-dimensional picture.

You already know that the Earth's surface emits infrared radiation, as does any heated object. Devices that are sensitive to infrared radiation are used in satellite-based remote sensing, and infrared radiation is increasingly used in thermal imaging devices; in Figure 8.17b the cooler temperatures indicate poor circulation in a human foot. Thermal imaging is also used to 'see in the dark' when conditions preclude the use of visible light, for example to detect people in smoke-filled buildings.

- Which carries the most energy: a photon of ultraviolet radiation, an X-ray photon or a gamma-ray photon?

□ The gamma-ray photon carries the most energy, then the X-ray photon and then the photon of ultraviolet radiation.

Most of the ultraviolet (UV) radiation experienced on Earth originates in the Sun and this causes skin to tan; an effect that can be reproduced using UV-emitting fluorescent tubes. In small doses this is usually harmless or even beneficial; for example, UV radiation is responsible for the production of vitamin D by the body. However, exposure to large doses of UV radiation can be dangerous, leading, among other effects, to melanoma (skin cancer).

X-rays have numerous uses, from medical imaging and radiation therapy in hospitals to luggage examination at airports. They are also used to detect subsurface defects in metals, and the technique of X-ray diffraction has been used to study the internal structure of matter on the atomic scale. X-rays were discovered by the German physicist Wilhelm Röntgen in 1895, and the usefulness of X-rays in diagnostic medicine was quickly realised. Unfortunately, early X-ray machines were unshielded and poorly controlled, so both patients and hospital staff were exposed to large doses of radiation. In the early days, the use of X-rays was limited to obtaining the image of an X-ray shadow on a photographic plate, but CT (computer tomography) scanning (Figure 8.17c) is now used to build up a detailed three-dimensional picture by producing images of 'slices' of the body, and even of soft tissue such as the brain.

Gamma rays are the most energetic form of electromagnetic radiation. Radioactive decays (discussed in Books 6 and 7) often produce gamma rays and, in medicine, gamma-ray cameras detect gamma rays from a radioactive 'tracer' ingested by the patient. In this way, the progress of the tracer through a particular organ can be monitored.

Question 8.4

Use Figure 8.16 to answer the following questions:

(a) A microwave oven cooks food by bombarding it with photons of microwave radiation. Roughly what is the energy of each of these photons in joules?

(b) During a dental X-ray, a patient is exposed to X-ray photons. Roughly what is the energy of each photon in electronvolts?

8.7   Summary of Chapter 8

Solar energy is the ultimate source of energy for life on Earth.

Solar energy can be exploited indirectly through food and fuels whose stored energy derives mainly from solar energy, or through renewable resources such as hydroelectricity and wind. It can also be exploited directly using solar collectors and solar cells.

Mass and energy are equivalent. The energy associated with mass m is given by Einstein's equation $E = mc^2$, where c is the speed of light.

The energy source within the Sun is the direct conversion of matter into energy, as part of a nuclear fusion process in which hydrogen is converted into helium.

Light propagates like a wave but it interacts with matter as though it is composed of a stream of particles, called photons.

Monochromatic light has a single colour and consists of identical photons that each have exactly the same energy. The amount of energy carried by a single photon is called a quantum. Quanta of visible radiation (light) have energies of around 2 to 3 eV.

White light comprises a range of different colours and can be dispersed to form a spectrum.

Each type of atom can be characterised by the energies of the photons it can absorb or emit. The spectral lines of atomic spectra provide a unique 'spectral fingerprint' of the atoms concerned.

Spectra may be plotted as graphs of intensity against photon energy. Such a graph is called a spectral distribution.

The continuous spectral distributions emitted by many hot objects have similar shapes. The higher the temperature of the object, the higher the energy at which the peak intensity in the spectral distribution occurs.

Visible light is just one part of the electromagnetic spectrum. Other forms of electromagnetic radiation share most of the properties of visible light, but they are characterised by different photon energies.

In studying this chapter you have performed a series of calculations, enabling you to estimate the lifetime of the Sun.

Chapter 9
Light as a wave

You know that light propagates like a wave, where a wave may be defined as a periodic, or regularly repeating, disturbance that transports energy from place to place. This chapter develops some of the terminology used to describe waves and then considers one of their important properties, the phenomenon called diffraction.

In addition, this chapter introduces the final new mathematical topic of Book 3 – the sine of an angle – and you will use previously developed skills associated with plotting straight-line graphs and finding and interpreting their gradients. However, you may be relieved to know that there is very little additional maths introduced in the rest of the course. Your 'mathematical weaponry' for studying S104 is almost complete. There will be plenty of opportunity to practise these skills throughout the course.

9.1   Describing waves

Before considering the wave nature of light and other forms of electromagnetic radiation, think about some other sorts of waves. Seismic waves (Book 2, Section 6.2.1) carry energy through the Earth from an earthquake and can cause damage to structures a considerable distance away. Another image conjured up by the word 'wave' is that of water waves on the sea (Figure 9.1).

Figure 9.1   Waves on the sea.

9.1.1   Wavelength and period

If you have ever stood on a beach, you will have seen or heard the crash of waves breaking onto the shore with a fairly regular time interval between one crash and the next. Each crash represents one wave crest breaking onto the shore and the time interval between them is called the **period** of the wave. In general, the period of a wave may be defined as the time between one part of the wave profile (say the crest) passing a fixed point in space and the next identical part of the wave profile (the next crest) passing the same fixed point. In this example, the fixed point is the shoreline.

■ What is the time interval between one trough of a wave and the next trough passing a fixed point?

☐ Since the troughs are spaced regularly between the crests, this time interval is also equal to the period of the wave.

Indeed, any point on a wave's profile can be used as a marker when measuring the wave's period. The important point is that the time interval between two successive *similar* points on the wave is used. Whether these successive points are both crests or both troughs, or both some similar intermediate point, is irrelevant – in each case, the time interval is the period of the wave.

The word wave is often used to describe a single crash onto the beach but it really refers to the entire sequence of crests and troughs, stretching away out to sea. You have already considered the way in which a wave's profile varies with time; now consider how it varies with distance. The distance between one wave crest and the next is called the **wavelength** of the wave (see Figure 9.2). In general, the wavelength of a wave is defined as the distance between one part of the wave profile, at a particular instant in time, and the next identical part of the wave profile at the same instant in time. Two adjacent crests of the wave are a convenient pair of locations to use for this definition, although any pair of similar points will do.

■ What is the distance between two adjacent troughs of a wave?

☐ By a similar argument to that used when discussing the period of a wave, the distance between two adjacent troughs is the same as the distance between two adjacent crests. So, this distance is clearly also equal to the wavelength of the wave.

You have probably noticed that the definitions for the period and the wavelength of a wave are rather similar. The period is a time interval and refers to instances separated in *time* but measured at a fixed point in space; the wavelength is a distance and refers to points separated in *space* but measured at a fixed instant in time. The relationship between them is clearly related to the speed at which the wave is moving – and that should come as no surprise since speed is the usual way of relating distances and times. The video sequence *Making Waves*, which you will watch in Activity 9.1, quantifies this relationship and develops the first key equation that describes wave propagation.

9.1.2   Amplitude

So much for the periodicity of waves; what of the assertion that they transport energy from one place to another? Again, waves on the sea provide a convenient example. Waves may be generated far out to sea by winds, where energy is imparted to the wave and transported by it until the wave finally breaks on the shore, and the energy is released.

■ What is the evidence for this release of energy when a wave breaks on the seashore?

☐ When the wave breaks, kinetic energy is imparted to pebbles and other debris, causing them to move. Also, the sound of the crash is heard, which is further evidence for the release of energy.

How does the energy transported by a wave on the sea depend on the properties of the wave? Again your experience probably tells you that, if the vertical distance between the trough and crest of a wave is greater (that is, if the waves are 'higher'), more energy is released as they crash onto the shore. As you will see at the beginning of the *Making Waves* video sequence, the waves on the sea during a storm tend to be very high. Storms can result in a great deal of damage to breakwaters and sea defences; clearly, higher waves carry more energy. The **amplitude** of a wave is conventionally defined as half the trough-to-crest height, or (equivalently) the maximum deviation of the wave from its mean position. Therefore, the amplitude of a wave is a measure of how much energy it carries. It turns out that the energy carried by a wave is actually proportional to the *square* of its amplitude, which explains why big breakers are so powerful.

The meanings of the wavelength and amplitude of a wave are summarised in Figure 9.2.

Figure 9.2   Wavelength and amplitude of a water wave.

The preceding discussion of waves in terms of natural water waves on the sea was rather qualitative. The problem is that waves on the sea are uncontrollable; they are not generally well behaved and regular, they are not strictly periodic, and one wave crest breaking on a beach is often quite different in nature to that immediately preceding or following it – just ask a surfer! This makes them difficult to study and therefore waves on the sea are not an ideal subject for examining wave behaviour in general. The aim here is to understand light waves but, unfortunately, these are even more difficult to study directly. Of the quantities mentioned above that characterise waves, the wave speed for light is extremely large, and the wavelength, period and amplitude are extremely small. Clearly, a more suitable, controlled situation is required which will enable wave behaviour to be examined more closely. In the video sequence *Making Waves* (Activity 9.1), a device known as a ripple tank is used to generate uniform, regular waves on the surface of water. These waves can be studied in a controlled manner, and the general principles learned can be applied to wave motion in general.

Activity 9.1   Making waves

We expect this activity will take you approximately 1 hour.

In this activity you will watch a video sequence which demonstrates important wave properties using a ripple tank. The video sequence also shows experiments with lasers and previews the practical work that you will do in Chapter 11 (Activity 11.1).

While watching the video sequence, you should make notes on the important properties of waves that are discussed. At certain points you will be instructed to stop the sequence and carry out tasks related to what you have just seen. Details of these tasks are given below, together with photographs of still-frames from the video sequence which you can use instead of taking measurements from the screen.

You should recall from Book 1, Box 3.3 that 1 μm = 1 × 10⁻⁶ m.

The video sequence abbreviates the word for a micrometre to a 'micron' and it introduces the word **reciprocal**. The reciprocal of a number is simply one divided by that number, so the reciprocal of 2 is $\frac{1}{2}$. In addition, the video sequence introduces the concept of **inverse proportionality**.

■ What is meant when two quantities are described as being directly proportional to each other?

☐ Two quantities are said to be directly proportional (or simply proportional) to each other if, when the value of one is multiplied (or divided) by a certain amount, the value of the other also becomes multiplied (or divided) by the same amount. The proportionality $y \propto x$ can be converted into the equation $y = kx$ by introducing a constant of proportionality, k (see Section 4.1.2).

There are many situations in which increasing or decreasing one quantity by a certain factor has the opposite effect on another quantity. For instance, if you double the speed v at which you travel, you halve the time t taken to complete a journey of a certain distance. If your speed *increases* by a factor of three, the time taken *decreases* by a factor of three. A relationship like this may be written as:

$$t \propto \frac{1}{v}$$

You would say that time t is inversely proportional to speed v and you can see from the relationship above that this is equivalent to saying that t is proportional to $\dfrac{1}{v}$.

An inverse proportionality can be converted into an equation by inserting a constant:

$$t = \frac{k}{v}$$

and in this case the constant of proportionality corresponds to the (constant) distance travelled (since $t = \dfrac{d}{v}$).

You should view the video sequence *Making Waves* now, pausing when instructed to do so to complete Tasks 1, 2 and 3.

Task 1   Determining the speed of a wave

Measure the wavelength and the period of the wave from the graphs shown on the video (or in Figure 9.3). What is the frequency of this wave? Using these data, calculate the speed of the wave illustrated by these two graphs.

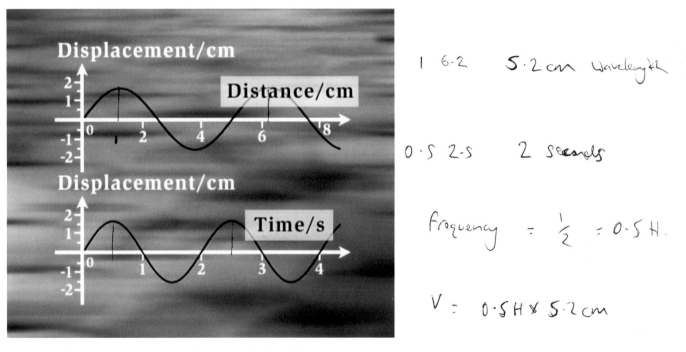

Figure 9.3   A copy of the graphs shown in the video sequence, for use with Task 1. Note that the mean displacement of this wave is zero. The displacement is measured above and below this mean level.

Now look at the comments on Task 1 at the end of this book and then return to the video sequence.

Table 9.1 Distance of spots from the centre of the diffraction pattern, using a grating with $d = 10.0\ \mu m$.

Order, n	Distance, s_n/mm
1	35
2	75
3	110
4	150
5	195
6	240

Task 2   The spread of a diffraction pattern: dependence on n

(a) Look at the diffraction pattern produced by the grating with $d = 10.0\ \mu m$, either on the computer or television screen or in Figure 9.4. Read off the distances of the first six spots from the centre of the diffraction pattern (indicated by the zero on the scale) and record this information in Table 9.1. Remember that s_n refers to the distance of the nth spot, so s_1 is the distance to the first order spot, s_2 the distance to the second order spot, and so on.

(b) Look at your results from (a). If the order n is doubled (say from $n = 1$ to $n = 2$ or from $n = 3$ to $n = 6$), what happens to the distance of the diffraction spot from the centre of the pattern? Bearing this in mind, what can you say about the dependence of s_n on n?

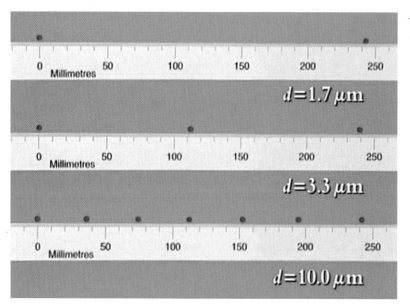

Figure 9.4   A copy of the diffraction patterns shown in the video sequence, for use with Tasks 2 and 3.

Task 3   The spread of a diffraction pattern: dependence on d

(a) Look at the diffraction patterns produced by gratings with $d = 3.3\ \mu m$ and $d = 1.7\ \mu m$ (i.e. 300 lines per mm and 600 lines per mm, respectively) either on the computer or television screen or in Figure 9.4. In each case, read off the distance of the first order spot from the centre of the diffraction pattern. Record your results, along with the corresponding distance for the first order diffraction spot from the grating with $d = 10.0\ \mu m$ (i.e. 100 lines per mm), in Table 9.2.

(b) The measurements in Table 9.2 are for a particular order of the diffraction pattern ($n = 1$) and red light of a particular wavelength, but they are for a range of values for the line spacing of the grating, d. How does the distance of the first order spot in the diffraction patterns vary with d? What do you conclude about the dependence of the spread of the diffraction pattern, as quantified by s_n, on the line spacing of the grating, d?

Look at the comments on Tasks 2 and 3 and then return to the video sequence for a summary of Activity 9.1 and a look forward to the practical work that you will do in Activity 11.1.

Table 9.2 Distance of the first order spots from the centre of the diffraction patterns, using three different gratings.

Line spacing, $d/\mu m$	Distance, s_1/mm
10.0	37
3.3	112
1.7	242

9.1.3   Frequency and wave speed

As you saw in the *Making Waves* video sequence, a wave may be characterised by its amplitude A, its wavelength λ, its **frequency** f (or period $T = \dfrac{1}{f}$), and its propagation speed v. The units of frequency can be thought of as 'cycles per second' or simply s^{-1}, and an equivalent unit is the **hertz** (symbol Hz), where $1\ \text{Hz} = 1\ s^{-1}$. (Remember that λ is the Greek letter lambda – wavelengths are always represented by this symbol.)

As you discovered in Activity 9.1 Task 1, a wave may be represented graphically either by its profile in space at a particular instant of time, or by its variation with time at a particular point in space. Examples of these two representations are shown in Figure 9.5. The speed of a wave v is related to its frequency and wavelength by the equation:

$$v = f\lambda \tag{9.1}$$

With λ in the SI units of metres and f in the SI units of hertz (or s^{-1}), the speed of the wave is expressed in the SI units of m s^{-1}. The speed of light (and all other electromagnetic radiation) in a vacuum is given the special symbol c and its value is $2.997\ 924\ 58 \times 10^8$ m s^{-1}. If light is travelling through a material such as air or glass, it travels at a slower speed.

■ What is the value of c to three significant figures?

☐ To three significant figures, the value rounds up to 3.00×10^8 m s^{-1} (see Book 1, Box 3.1 for advice on rounding).

So for light, or any other electromagnetic radiation, Equation 9.1 can be written as:

$$c = f\lambda \tag{9.2}$$

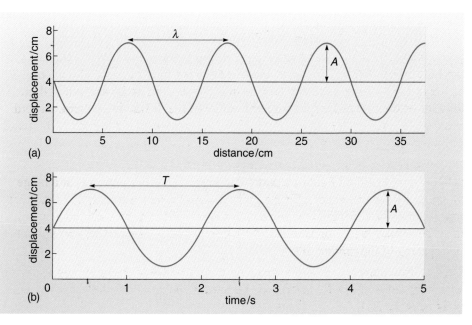

(a)

(b)

Figure 9.5   The space and time representations of a wave. In each case, the horizontal line at 4 cm represents the mean displacement of the wave. (a) A graph showing a wave profile at a fixed instant of time, illustrating how the displacement varies with position. The distance between two adjacent positions where the profile has the same displacement, and where the displacement is changing in the same way, is equal to the wavelength λ. (b) A graph showing how the displacement at a fixed point in space varies with time. The interval between two successive times when the displacement is the same, and when the displacement is changing in the same way, is equal to the period T.

Five complete cycles of a water wave travel past a fixed point in two seconds.

(a) What is the period of this wave?

(b) What is its frequency?

Figure 9.5b shows the time representation of a particular wave. Using only the information in Figure 9.5b determine, if possible: (a) the period, (b) the frequency, (c) the amplitude, and (d) the speed of this wave.

You saw in Activity 9.1 that a red laser beam consists of light with a longer wavelength than that of a green laser beam. What does this tell you about the relative frequencies of red light and green light?

9.2   The diffraction of light

As you saw in Activity 9.1, **diffraction** is the process by which waves are 'spread out' by apertures (slits) whose size d is similar to the wavelength λ of the wave. A **diffraction pattern** contains places where the waves reinforce each other (diffraction maxima) and places where the waves cancel out (diffraction minima). The spread of a diffraction pattern increases both as the wavelength is *increased* and as the aperture size is *decreased*.

> All waves can be diffracted and this is a defining property of waves in general.

9.2.1   Diffraction by a diffraction grating

A **diffraction grating** is a device with many parallel, equally spaced lines ruled on its surface (Figure 9.6), so the light is diffracted by *many* parallel apertures. If a diffraction grating has a spacing d between adjacent lines, the number of lines per unit distance is $\frac{1}{d}$. Conversely, the spacing between adjacent lines is:

$$d = \frac{1}{\text{number of lines per unit distance}}$$

■ If a diffraction grating has 500 lines per mm ruled on its surface, how far apart are the individual lines?

☐ The spacing between lines is:

$$d = \frac{1}{500 \text{ mm}^{-1}} = 0.002 \text{ mm} = 2 \times 10^{-3} \text{ mm} = 2 \times 10^{-6} \text{ m}$$

Since $1 \text{ μm} = 1 \times 10^{-6}$ m, this means that $d = 2$ μm.

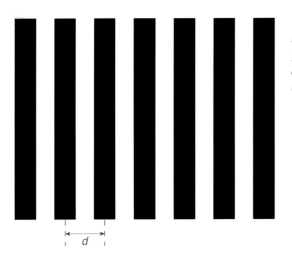

Figure 9.6   Sketch of a section of a diffraction grating (highly magnified); d is the spacing between adjacent lines.

When a diffraction grating is illuminated with a laser (which provides a monochromatic source of light), the diffraction pattern produced consists of a series of spots, spaced symmetrically either side of the central position. These spots are called **diffraction orders**, the one in the centre being called the zero order, the pair on either side of it the first order, the next pair of spots outside those the second order, and so on. The spread of the spots increases both as the wavelength of the light is *increased* and as the spacing between the lines of the grating is *decreased*.

As you saw in Activity 9.1, the spread of a diffraction pattern produced by a diffraction grating may be characterised by the distance s_n of the nth spot away from the centre of the pattern. For small values of this distance, s_n is proportional to both the order n and the wavelength λ of the light, but *inversely* proportional to the spacing d between the lines of the grating. The following relationship summarises this information:

$$s_n \propto \frac{n\lambda}{d}$$

However, as Activity 9.1 indicated, this is only an approximation to the real situation and holds true only when the distances are small.

9.2.2   The sine of an angle

To obtain an accurate description of the diffraction pattern produced when light of wavelength λ passes through a diffraction grating of spacing d, a brief mathematical detour is needed into the world of angles and right-angled triangles. If necessary, refresh your memory about angles and degrees by rereading Box 8.1 of Book 1.

■   What is a right angle?

☐   It is the angle between two directions that are perpendicular to each other, with a value of 90°.

Look at the triangle in Figure 9.7a. This is called a **right-angled triangle** because one of its angles is a right angle.

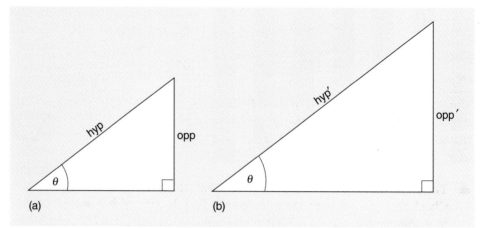

Figure 9.7   Two triangles of different sizes but with the same angles as each other. The squares in the bottom right-hand corner of the triangles denote right angles.

Another of the angles in the triangle is labelled θ, which is the Greek letter theta (pronounced 'thee-ta' where the 'th' is soft as in 'think') and is frequently used to denote angles. The side of the triangle facing the right angle is the longest of the three sides and is called the **hypotenuse**, labelled hyp in the diagram. The side of the triangle that is opposite the angle θ is labelled accordingly as opp. A similar triangle can also be drawn, with the same angles as the first triangle, but with the length of each side increased (Figure 9.7b). The sides of this triangle are labelled with the same abbreviations as the first, but with the symbol $'$ (prime) added.

- ■ Measure the length of the sides labelled opp and hyp in Figure 9.7a and calculate the value of $\dfrac{\text{opp}}{\text{hyp}}$.

- ☐ opp = 3.0 cm and hyp = 5.0 cm, so $\dfrac{\text{opp}}{\text{hyp}} = \dfrac{3.0\,\text{cm}}{5.0\,\text{cm}} = 0.60$.

- ■ Now measure the lengths of the sides labelled opp$'$ and hyp$'$ in Figure 9.7b and calculate the value of $\dfrac{\text{opp}'}{\text{hyp}'}$.

- ☐ opp$'$ = 4.5 cm and hyp$'$ = 7.5 cm, so $\dfrac{\text{opp}'}{\text{hyp}'} = \dfrac{4.5\,\text{cm}}{7.5\,\text{cm}} = 0.60$.

So the length of the side opposite the angle θ divided by the length of the hypotenuse is the same for the two triangles. If the angle θ and hence the shape of the triangle had been different, the value of $\dfrac{\text{opp}}{\text{hyp}}$ would have been different too. However, each angle θ gives rise to a unique value for $\dfrac{\text{opp}}{\text{hyp}}$. This result is so important that, for an angle in a right-angled triangle, the length of the opposite side divided by the length of the hypotenuse is given the special name **sine**, pronounced 'sign' and often abbreviated to 'sin':

$$\sin \theta = \frac{\text{opp}}{\text{hyp}} \qquad\qquad (9.3)$$

Note that sin θ is defined with respect to a particular angle in the triangle. If the other angle in the triangle had been considered, $\frac{\text{opp}}{\text{hyp}}$ and hence the sine of the angle would have been different.

The sine of an angle is one of several so-called trigonometric functions (you might also have heard of cosine and tangent). You don't normally have to measure the lengths of the sides of a right-angled triangle in order to find the sine of an angle; the values are stored in your calculator.

■ The angle θ in Figures 9.7a and 9.7b is 36.9° to three significant figures. Check that you can use your calculator to find the sine of this angle (you will probably need to use a key marked sin and you may also need to check that your calculator is operating in degrees mode).

☐ You should have got a value of 0.600 to three significant figures, the same result as you obtained from measuring the sides of the triangles. If you got a different answer you may need to check the mode of your calculator. Check the operating instructions now.

Since the sine of an angle is obtained by dividing one length by another length, the sine itself does not have any units.

Question 9.4

Use your calculator to find the sine of the following angles (quote your answers to three decimal places):

(a) 10°; (b) 60°; (c) 30°; (d) 0°

9.2.3 An equation for diffraction

The exact relationship between the wavelength λ and the line spacing of the diffraction grating d depends on the **angle of diffraction** θ_n of the nth order. As Figure 9.8 shows, the angle of diffraction is defined as the angle between the straight-through position and that at which a spot is found in the diffraction pattern.

The equation relating the angle of diffraction θ_n to the wavelength λ, grating line spacing d, and order n of the diffraction pattern is:

$$\sin \theta_n = \frac{n\lambda}{d} \qquad\qquad (9.4)$$

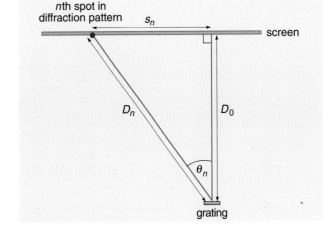

Figure 9.8 The angle of diffraction θ_n of the nth spot in a diffraction pattern.

This is an important equation and you will use it in Activities 9.2 and 11.1 to determine the wavelength of light.

Equation 9.4 may be derived from a consideration of the geometry of the situation and an understanding of the behaviour of light waves. The derivation is not given here since it would be a lengthy detour from the main story. However, you can reassure yourself by confirming (by following the argument below) that Equation 9.4 is approximately equivalent to the relationship $s_n \propto \dfrac{n\lambda}{d}$ for small values of s_n. This is the result you observed in Activity 9.1.

■ Use Figure 9.8 and the definition of the sine of an angle to write an expression for $\sin \theta_n$ in terms of s_n and D_n.

☐ $\sin \theta_n = \dfrac{\text{opp}}{\text{hyp}} = \dfrac{s_n}{D_n}$

Substituting $\dfrac{s_n}{D_n}$ in place of $\sin \theta_n$ in Equation 9.4 gives:

$$\frac{s_n}{D_n} = \frac{n\lambda}{d} \tag{9.5}$$

When s_n is small, the distance of each spot away from the grating D_n is approximately the same in each case, and roughly equal to D_0, the perpendicular distance between the grating and the screen. In this case Equation 9.5 becomes:

$$\frac{s_n}{D_0} = \frac{n\lambda}{d} \quad \text{or} \quad s_n = D_0 \times \frac{n\lambda}{d}$$

Since D_0 is a constant, this can be written as a proportionality: $s_n \propto \dfrac{n\lambda}{d}$. This is the same result as you observed in the laser experiments in Activity 9.1.

Activity 9.2   Determining the wavelength of laser light

We expect this activity will take you approximately 30 minutes.

In this activity you will use the results from Activity 9.1 to determine the wavelength of the red light produced by the laser. The activity will give you practice at using the sine function, plotting graphs and measuring gradients, and relating a straight line on a graph to the equation for the line.

Start by looking at Equation 9.4 more closely to see how it can be used to find a value for the wavelength of light:

$$\sin \theta_n = \frac{n\lambda}{d} \tag{9.4}$$

The angles of diffraction θ_n can be measured for various values of n (the order of the diffraction pattern). The line spacing d can be measured, using a microscope for instance. In Equation 9.4, the only quantity that cannot be measured directly is λ – the wavelength of the light. Here then is a means of calculating the wavelength of the light used to produce the diffraction pattern.

Task I   Calculating $\sin \theta_n$

In Task 2 of Activity 9.1, you measured the distances of the diffraction orders from the centre of the diffraction pattern when a red laser beam illuminated a diffraction grating with $d = 10.0 \, \mu\text{m}$. The angles of diffraction corresponding to these orders (measured to the nearest half-degree) are shown in Table 9.3. Complete the table by calculating $\sin \theta_n$ for each order. (Record each value of $\sin \theta_n$ to three decimal places.)

Check your answers with those in the comments on Task 1 at the end of this book before moving on to Task 2.

Table 9.3 Diffraction data obtained with a red laser illuminating a grating with $d = 10.0$ μm.

Order, n	θ_n/degrees	sin θ_n
0	0.0	0
1	3.5	0.061
2	7.5	0.131
3	11.0	0.191
4	15.0	0.259
5	18.5	0.317
6	22.5	0.383

Task 2   Plotting a graph

Equation 9.4 states that $\sin\theta_n = \dfrac{n\lambda}{d}$. For this set of data, the wavelength λ and the line spacing of the grating d do not change. The only quantities that vary from one measurement to the next are sin θ_n and n. Bearing this in mind, use the values in your completed Table 9.3 to plot a graph of sin θ_n against n on Figure 9.9.

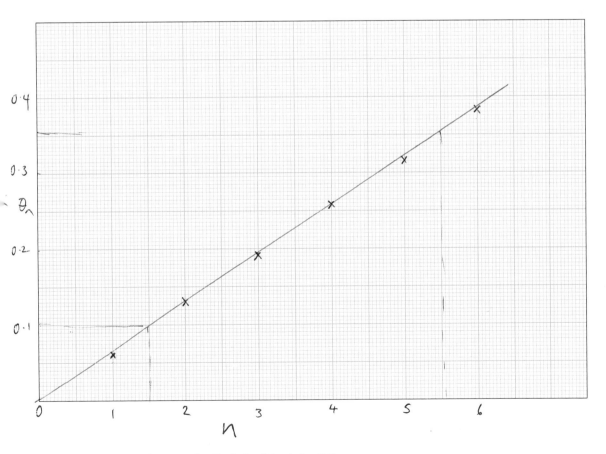

Figure 9.9   Graph paper for Task 2 of Activity 9.2.

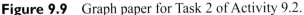

$$5.5 - 1.5 = 4$$
$$0.355 - 0.1 = 0.255$$

As you learned in Book 2, Box 6.1, it is conventional to plot the dependent variable (in this case, $\sin \theta_n$) up the vertical axis of the graph, and the independent variable (in this case, n), along the horizontal axis. Choose a scale that uses as fully as possible the entire graph paper, but ensure that each centimetre division on the scale represents a sensible number. For instance, two 1 cm divisions for every 0.1 change in $\sin \theta_n$ would be sensible since each division then represents 0.05. Three 1 cm divisions for every 0.1 change would not be sensible, since each division would then represent 0.033 33 and it would be more difficult to plot the data.

Task 3 The best-fit straight line

When you have plotted the points, draw what you consider to be the best-fit straight line corresponding to these data points. Remember that the best-fit straight line is the one that passes closest to most of the data points. Inevitably, most of the points will not fall exactly on the straight line (although some may, by chance), but you should attempt to draw the line so that the points are fairly evenly distributed on either side of it.

Check that your graph agrees with the one in the comments on Task 3 at the end of this book before moving on to Task 4.

Task 4 The gradient of the graph

The graph you have plotted of $\sin \theta_n$ against n is a straight line passing through the origin, which means that $\sin \theta_n$ is proportional to n. This is what you might expect from Equation 9.4, $\sin \theta_n = \dfrac{n\lambda}{d}$, because if you write the equation as $\sin \theta_n = \left(\dfrac{\lambda}{d}\right) \times n$, and remember that both λ and d are constant for this set of data, you can see that $\sin \theta_n \propto n$, or $\sin \theta_n = mn$, where the constant of proportionality $m = \dfrac{\lambda}{d}$. This shows that there is a straightforward relationship between $\sin \theta_n$ and n, when both λ and d are constant, as is the case here. So Equation 9.4 is the equation of the straight line obtained when $\sin \theta_n$ is plotted against n. Writing Equation 9.4 as $\sin \theta_n = \left(\dfrac{\lambda}{d}\right) \times n$ makes it clear that the gradient of the graph you have just plotted is equal to $\dfrac{\lambda}{d}$.

You should now measure the gradient of the graph (see Book 2, Box 6.1 if you need a reminder of how to do this) and use this value to calculate the wavelength of the red laser light. (Remember $d = 10.0$ μm for this grating.)

Now look at the comments on Task 4 at the end of this book.

The procedure described in Activity 9.2 is all very well with just a single wavelength of light, such as a laser beam, but what about 'white light' which contains a whole range of wavelengths? As you saw at the end of the *Making Waves* video sequence in Activity 9.1, a diffraction grating effectively spreads out the spectrum of the light source in each order of the diffraction pattern, apart from the zero order. The individual orders are spread out into a rainbow of colours, and each colour in the spectrum of the light source appears at a specific position within each order of the diffraction pattern. In this case, Equation 9.4 can be applied as well, but the measurements must always refer to the same feature in each order of the spectrum (such as a particular spectral line). You know that the blue lines in each order of the diffraction pattern of an energy-saving bulb, for instance, must all correspond to the same wavelength of light – that's what makes them blue! So, if the angles of diffraction for the blue lines in the different orders are measured, the wavelength corresponding to blue light can be calculated. You will do this in Activity 11.1.

Question 9.5

Yellow light of wavelength 572 nm passes through a diffraction grating and the resulting diffraction pattern is observed. The fourth order image has an angle of diffraction of 43.7°. What is the diffraction grating's line spacing?

9.3 The frequency and wavelength of electromagnetic radiation

As you have seen, diffraction is one way of determining the wavelength of a wave when this cannot be measured directly. When light is diffracted by a grating, the angles of diffraction of successive orders in the diffraction pattern are determined by just two factors: the spacing d of the lines in the grating, and the wavelength λ of the light. So, by using $\sin\theta_n = \dfrac{n\lambda}{d}$, and measuring the spacing d, the wavelength of light may be determined. Having determined the wavelength in this way, the equation $c = f\lambda$ can then be used to calculate the frequency of the light. You are now in a position to add both frequency and wavelength scales to the electromagnetic spectrum that you saw in Chapter 8.

The familiar rainbow of colours occupies a very narrow region of the electromagnetic spectrum, with wavelengths in the range from around 4×10^{-7} m (violet) to 7×10^{-7} m (red). The frequencies of these visible limits are about 7.5×10^{14} Hz (violet) and 4.3×10^{14} Hz (red). As shown in Figure 9.10, the wavelength of electromagnetic radiation decreases in progressing from radio waves, through microwaves, infrared radiation, light, ultraviolet radiation and X-rays to gamma rays. Conversely, the frequency of electromagnetic radiation increases in progressing through the same sequence.

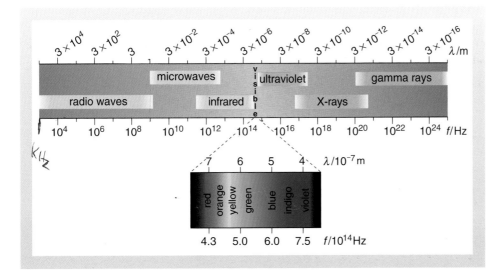

Figure 9.10 The electromagnetic spectrum showing frequency and wavelength scales, with the visible region of the spectrum expanded.

■ Remembering the relationship $c = f\lambda$, are the wavelength and frequency scales in Figure 9.10 consistent with the value of the speed of light ($c = 3 \times 10^8$ m s^{-1})?

☐ Yes. For example, the boundary between ultraviolet radiation and X-rays is shown to occur around a frequency of 1×10^{17} Hz, and a wavelength of 3×10^{-9} m. Multiplying these two numbers gives the speed of light, as required: $(1 \times 10^{17}$ Hz$) \times (3 \times 10^{-9}$ m$) = 3 \times 10^8$ m s^{-1}. (Remember that the unit Hz is equivalent to s^{-1}.)

Question 9.6

(a) On the frequency axis of Figure 9.10, where would 1 kHz, 1 MHz and 1 GHz occur?

(b) On the wavelength axis, where would 1 nm, 1 μm and 1 mm occur?

Question 9.7

(a) A microwave oven operates at a frequency of 2.45 GHz. What is the wavelength of these microwaves?

(b) Technetium-99m, commonly used as a radioactive tracer, produces gamma rays of wavelength 8.8×10^{-12} m. What is their frequency?

(You should assume that the speed of electromagnetic radiation, c, is 3.00×10^8 m s^{-1}.)

9.4   Summary of Chapter 9

The wavelength of a wave is the distance between two neighbouring, equivalent points on the wave profile and has the symbol λ.

The frequency of a wave is the number of cycles of the wave that pass a given point in one second and has the symbol f.

The period of a wave, T, is the time taken for one complete cycle of the wave to pass a fixed point, and is related to its frequency by $T = \dfrac{1}{f}$.

The speed of any wave, v, is related to its frequency and wavelength by the equation $v = f\lambda$.

The wavelength and frequency of an electromagnetic wave are related by the equation $c = f\lambda$ where c is the speed of light and has a value of 3.00×10^8 m s^{-1} to three significant figures.

The sine of an angle θ in a right-angled triangle is defined by

$$\sin\theta = \frac{\text{opposite}}{\text{hypotenuse}}$$

where opposite is the length of the side opposite θ and hypotenuse is the length of the side opposite the right angle.

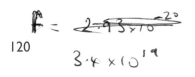

Waves may be diffracted by apertures whose size is similar to the wavelength of the wave.

For a diffraction grating with a line spacing d, illuminated with a laser beam of wavelength λ, the diffraction pattern observed on a distant screen consists of a series of spots, known as diffraction orders. The angle of diffraction of the nth order either side of the centre is given by:

$$\sin \theta_n = \frac{n\lambda}{d}$$

When a diffraction grating is illuminated by a light source containing a range of wavelengths, the different wavelengths are effectively spread out in the diffraction pattern. Each order of the diffraction pattern consists of a spectrum of the light source.

Different regions of the electromagnetic spectrum are distinguished by the different wavelengths and frequencies of the radiation. Radio waves have the longest wavelength and the lowest frequency. Moving towards shorter wavelengths and higher frequencies, we have microwaves, infrared radiation, light, ultraviolet radiation, and X-rays. Gamma rays have the shortest wavelength and highest frequency.

In studying this chapter you have plotted a graph and found its gradient. You have related the equation for a straight line to the line drawn on the graph.

Chapter 10
Light as particles

Having discussed the wave-like propagation of light and other electromagnetic radiation, it is time to return to a consideration of its particle-like interaction with matter. This chapter is concerned with photons, which, as you have seen, are particles of electromagnetic radiation. In the interaction of light with matter it is the photon's energy that is important. So perhaps the first question to address is: 'How is this energy related to the wave properties of electromagnetic radiation?'

Chapter 9 noted that waves transport energy from one place to another, and that the amount of energy carried by a wave depends on the wave's amplitude. In the case of sound waves, the energy of the wave manifests itself as the loudness of the sound – a louder sound clearly transports more energy than a quieter sound and so must correspond to a wave of larger amplitude. Similarly, you might expect that the energy of a light wave is related to its brightness, i.e. to the intensity of the illumination.

While this is true for electromagnetic radiation, it is not the end of the story. Problems with this simple picture for the energy carried by light waves became apparent as a result of a series of experiments that were done between 1887 and 1902. These experiments, first by Heinrich Hertz, then by J. J. Thomson (the English physicist who discovered the electron) and finally by the German physicist Philipp Lenard, led to the discovery of a phenomenon known as the photoelectric effect.

10.1   The interaction of electromagnetic radiation and matter

Experiments show that when some metals are illuminated by a strong source of electromagnetic radiation, electrons are emitted from the metal's surface. This is known as the **photoelectric effect**. Certain metals respond better than others; some emit electrons when illuminated with visible light, whereas for other metals only ultraviolet radiation causes electrons to be emitted. The electrons that are ejected, called **photoelectrons**, do not all emerge with the same kinetic energy, but there is a well-defined maximum kinetic energy that depends on the type of radiation and the type of metal used. The results of the photoelectric effect are shown schematically in Figure 10.1.

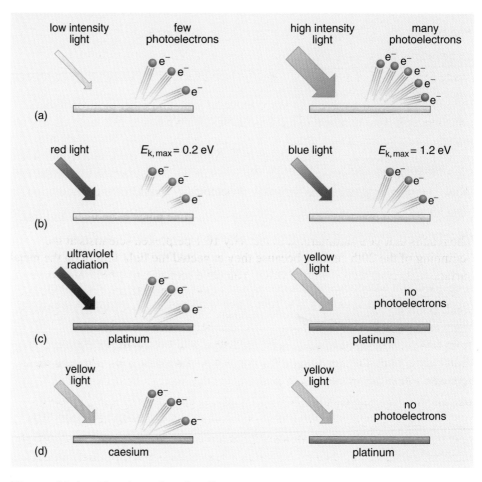

Figure 10.1   The photoelectric effect.

(a) Changing the intensity of the radiation. The number of photoelectrons emitted by the metal increases as the intensity of the radiation is increased, but the range of energies of the photoelectrons remains exactly the same.

(b) Increasing the frequency of the radiation. The higher the frequency of the radiation falling onto the metal, the higher the maximum kinetic energy $E_{k, max}$ of the photoelectrons. In this example, increasing the frequency of the light from red to blue increases the maximum kinetic energy of the photoelectrons from 0.2 eV to 1.2 eV.

(c) Decreasing the frequency of the radiation. There is a lower limit to the frequency of the radiation, below which no photoelectrons are emitted. In this example, when platinum is illuminated with ultraviolet radiation, photoelectrons are emitted. However, when platinum is illuminated with yellow light, no photoelectrons are emitted, whatever the intensity of the source.

(d) Changing the metal. The lower limit to the frequency is different for different metals. In this example, when caesium is illuminated with yellow light, photoelectrons are emitted. However, when platinum is illuminated with the same source of light, no photoelectrons are emitted.

Activity 10.1 The photoelectric effect – some surprising results

We expect this activity will take you approximately 15 minutes.

Study Figure 10.1 and its caption and then summarise the possible effects on photoelectron emission of:

(a) illuminating a metal with light of a greater intensity

(b) illuminating a metal with light of a greater frequency

(c) changing the metal.

Now look at the comments on this activity at the end of this book.

The results that you summarised in Activity 10.1 perplexed scientists at the beginning of the 20th century because they expected the light falling on the metal surface to interact as if it were a wave. You have seen already that water waves with a large amplitude impart more kinetic energy to pebbles on a beach than do small ripples. Well, a light wave with a large amplitude corresponds to an intense light, so the scientists expected that high intensity light would eject electrons from a metal with greater kinetic energy than would low intensity light, and they didn't expect that the frequency of the light would have an effect. Yet exactly the opposite was observed to be the case.

Perhaps the most startling result is that shown in Figure 10.1c. Shining yellow light on platinum does not result in the production of photoelectrons, no matter how intense the light source. However, changing the yellow light for a source of ultraviolet radiation (even a low intensity one) results in the immediate production of photoelectrons. Once again, comparing light waves to sound waves, it is like an imaginary situation where increasing the loudness of a sound wave has no effect, whereas increasing the pitch (frequency) of the sound wave has a marked and immediate effect, no matter how quietly the higher-pitched note is played.

10.2 The energy of a photon

In 1900, the German physicist Max Planck suggested that light could only interact with matter in discrete quanta with specific amounts of energy. Building on this idea, which is developed further in Book 7, the first satisfactory explanation for the photoelectric effect was proposed by Albert Einstein in 1905. He argued that a whole quantum of light energy was absorbed by a single electron in the metal. (The quantum of light energy was subsequently named the photon, in 1926, after further experiments revealed that light quanta possessed other particle-like attributes.) Einstein's key idea, expressed in modern terms, was that the energy of a single photon is proportional to the frequency of the light wave that is used to characterise its propagation, that is $E_{ph} \propto f$ or:

$$E_{ph} = hf \tag{10.1}$$

This equation states that the energy E_{ph} carried by a photon of light (or any other electromagnetic radiation) is equal to a certain constant h multiplied by the frequency f of the light. The constant represented by the symbol h is called the **Planck constant**.

■ What is the SI unit of the Planck constant?

☐ The SI unit of energy is the joule and frequency is measured in hertz.
Equation 10.1 may be rearranged as $h = \dfrac{E_{ph}}{f}$, so the unit of h can be expressed as joules per hertz (J Hz^{-1}). However, 1 Hz = 1 s^{-1}, so conversely 1 Hz^{-1} = 1 s. The SI unit for the Planck constant is therefore the joule second (J s).

The value of the Planck constant h is 6.63×10^{-34} J s to three significant figures. However, energies expressed in electronvolts (eV) are often more appropriate and, for this reason, an equally valid unit for the Planck constant is electronvolts per hertz (eV Hz^{-1}).

Since 1 eV = 1.602×10^{-19} J (from Section 7.4), 1 J = $\dfrac{1}{1.602 \times 10^{-19}}$ eV = 6.242×10^{18} eV so

$$h = (6.63 \times 10^{-34} \times 6.242 \times 10^{18}) \text{ eV s}$$
$$= 4.14 \times 10^{-15} \text{ eV Hz}^{-1} \text{ to three significant figures}$$

This value could be written as $h = 4.14 \times 10^{-15}$ eV s, but the units are more commonly expressed as eV Hz^{-1}.

■ By considering the relative frequencies of ultraviolet and infrared radiation (Figure 9.10) and using Equation 10.1, which carries the greater energy: a photon of ultraviolet radiation or a photon of infrared radiation?

☐ Since ultraviolet radiation has a higher frequency than infrared radiation, and the energy of a photon is proportional to the frequency of the radiation ($E_{ph} \propto f$), a photon of ultraviolet radiation must carry a greater amount of energy than a photon of infrared radiation.

Equation 10.1 links photon energy (characteristic of the particle model of light) with frequency (characteristic of the wave model). This equation and Equation 9.2, which relates frequency and wavelength, can be used to find an expression for the energy of a photon in terms of its wavelength. (Refer back to Section 5.6 if you need to remind yourself how to combine algebraic equations.) Equation 10.1 states that the energy of a photon of electromagnetic radiation is related to its frequency by $E_{ph} = hf$. Equation 9.2 shows that the frequency, wavelength and speed of an electromagnetic wave are related by $c = f\lambda$, where c is the speed of light. Equation 9.2 can be rearranged to make f the subject by dividing both sides of the equation by λ, giving $f = \dfrac{c}{\lambda}$. Substituting this equation for f into Equation 10.1 gives:

$$E_{ph} = h \times \frac{c}{\lambda} \quad \text{or} \quad E_{ph} = \frac{hc}{\lambda} \tag{10.2}$$

Question 10.1

An X-ray photon has an energy of 511 keV. What is the corresponding wavelength of this radiation? You may assume that the Planck constant $h = 4.14 \times 10^{-15}$ eV Hz^{-1}, and that the speed of light $c = 3.00 \times 10^8$ m s^{-1}.

10.3   Understanding the photoelectric effect

Once Einstein had suggested that light quanta (i.e. photons) carry a discrete amount of energy, with a value related to the frequency of the electromagnetic wave used to characterise its propagation, the photoelectric effect was explained simply by applying the principle of conservation of energy. Einstein proposed that there was a minimum energy E_0 required to release an electron from a metal. He supposed that this value was a constant for a particular metal, but varied from one metal to another. So, when a photon is absorbed by an electron within a metal, there are two possible outcomes.

1   If the energy of the photon is less than E_0, no photoelectron is emitted; the photon is simply absorbed, increasing the internal energy of the metal.

2   If the energy of the photon is greater than E_0, some of the photon's energy is 'used up' in freeing the electron from the metal and, if there is any energy 'left over', this will appear as the kinetic energy of the photoelectron that is emitted. In terms of the law of conservation of energy:

$$(\text{energy of photon}) = \left(\begin{array}{c}\text{energy needed to} \\ \text{release photoelectron}\end{array}\right) + \left(\begin{array}{c}\text{kinetic energy of} \\ \text{emitted photoelectron}\end{array}\right) \quad (10.3)$$

Now, when a metal is illuminated with photons of a single energy (and therefore radiation of a single frequency), such that E_{ph} is greater than E_0, photoelectrons are emitted with a *range* of kinetic energies.

■   The input energy is the same in each case (all the photons have the same energy) so what does the fact that photoelectrons are emitted with a range of energies suggest about the energy needed to release different photoelectrons? (*Hint*: consider Equation 10.3.)

☐   Different amounts of energy are required to release different electrons from the metal. As you learn more about atomic structure in Books 4 and 7, you will discover that this is a very reasonable suggestion.

The photoelectrons that emerge with the smallest kinetic energy are the ones that needed the largest amount of energy to free them from the metal; the photoelectrons that emerge with the largest kinetic energy are those that needed the smallest amount of energy to free them from the metal. The *smallest* amount of energy needed to free an electron from the metal is E_0, so in this case Equation 10.3 can be written in symbols as:

$$E_{ph} = E_0 + E_{k,\,max} \quad (10.4)$$

where $E_{k,\,max}$ is the maximum kinetic energy acquired by any photoelectron. Rearranging Equation 10.4 to make $E_{k,\,max}$ the subject gives:

$$E_{k,\,max} = E_{ph} - E_0 \quad (10.5)$$

Equation 10.5 is a statement, using modern symbols, of Einstein's explanation of the photoelectric effect. As noted already, this equation is nothing more than an application of the law of conservation of energy. Now, how do Einstein's ideas explain the observations shown in Figure 10.1? Taking each part of the figure in turn:

(a) The fact that the number of photoelectrons increases with the intensity of the light is explained by each photon liberating exactly one photoelectron. A higher intensity of light implies that more photons are present, so more photoelectrons are ejected.

(b) The fact that the maximum kinetic energy of the photoelectrons depends on the frequency of the light is explained because photons corresponding to radiation of a higher frequency carry more energy. So, after energy E_0 has been used by an electron to escape from the metal, there is more energy left over to appear as kinetic energy of the photoelectron. Note that each photon interacts with one and only one electron, so the surplus energy cannot be used to release further photoelectrons.

(c) The fact that there is a lower limit for the frequency of radiation, below which no photoelectrons are emitted, is built into Einstein's assumptions. Since the minimum energy required to eject electrons from a particular metal is E_0, the minimum frequency radiation needed to do this is $\dfrac{E_0}{h}$.

(d) The lower limit of frequency is different for different metals simply because different metals each have a different value of E_0. In the example shown, caesium has a lower value of E_0 than platinum, so the lower limit for the frequency of radiation which can eject electrons from its surface is also lower.

■ A metal surface is illuminated with photons of blue light, each of which carry 3.0 eV of energy. If a photoelectron is emitted with a kinetic energy of 0.7 eV, how much energy was required to remove it from the metal?

☐ The energy of the absorbed photon is divided between the energy needed to liberate the electron from the metal and the kinetic energy imparted to the photoelectron. So, in this case, the energy that was required to remove the electron from the metal is simply $(3.0 - 0.7)$ eV $= 2.3$ eV.

In the following Questions 10.2 and 10.3 you may assume that the Planck constant $h = 4.14 \times 10^{-15}$ eV Hz^{-1}, and that the speed of light $c = 3.00 \times 10^8$ m s^{-1}.

Question 10.2

The minimum energy required to eject an electron from a tungsten surface is 4.6 eV. What would be the maximum kinetic energy of the photoelectrons produced when ultraviolet radiation of frequency 1.5×10^{15} Hz is shone on a tungsten surface? Express your answer in eV.

Question 10.3

Photoelectrons with a maximum kinetic energy of 6.30 eV are emitted from a metal when it is illuminated by ultraviolet radiation with a wavelength of 152 nm.

(a) What is the energy of the incident photons in electronvolts?

(b) What is the wavelength of the radiation corresponding to the lowest energy photons that can free electrons from the metal?

(c) Why are no photoelectrons emitted when infrared radiation is shone on this metal?

Activity 4.1   Keeping track of symbols, units and equations – Part 4

We expect this part of the activity will take you approximately 10 minutes.

No more new symbols, equations or units are introduced in the rest of Book 3, so this is a good point to check that your glossary is up to date. You may like to continue adding to this glossary as the course progresses.

There are no comments on this activity.

10.4   Summary of Chapter 10

Each photon carries an amount of energy E_{ph} that is determined by the frequency f of the radiation used to characterise its propagation, namely:

$$E_{ph} = hf$$

where h is the Planck constant and equal to 4.14×10^{-15} eV Hz^{-1}, or 6.63×10^{-34} J s.

In the photoelectric effect, photons eject electrons from the surfaces of metals. The maximum kinetic energy ($E_{k, max}$) of the photoelectrons depends on the frequency of the radiation, but not on its intensity. No electrons are emitted if the photon energy is below a certain minimum value E_0, which varies from one metal to another. From a consideration of the conservation of energy:

$$E_{k, max} = E_{ph} - E_0$$

In studying this chapter you have summarised information presented in a complicated figure and its caption.

Chapter 11
Wave–particle duality

Having considered the wave-like propagation of light (Chapter 9) and its particle-like interaction with matter (Chapter 10), you are now ready to tie the two together. You will do this by carrying out an experiment that relies on both the particle and wave descriptions of light. Towards the end of this chapter you will see that matter (e.g. electrons) can also behave both like particles and like waves, given the appropriate conditions.

11.1   Light as waves and particles

You have seen that Equation 10.1 ($E_{ph} = hf$) links the particle and wave models of light. As noted earlier, light is neither a wave nor a particle but, in most situations, its behaviour can be described in terms of one or the other. The words 'wave' and 'particle' bring to mind images of phenomena that are familiar from everyday experience, such as waves on the sea and snooker balls moving around a table. There is really no reason to expect something like electromagnetic radiation to behave in as simple a manner as either of these. However, it is remarkable that simple wave ideas can be used when considering the propagation of electromagnetic radiation and simple particle ideas can be used when considering its interaction with matter. In this way we can model the complex physical world with simple, understandable concepts.

In Activity 11.1 you will carry out an experiment that relies on both the wave-like propagation and the particle-like interaction of light. You will collect your own data and then, using Equation 9.4 ($\sin\theta_n = \dfrac{n\lambda}{d}$), Equation 9.2 ($c = f\lambda$) and Equation 10.1 ($E_{ph} = hf$), you will determine values for the wavelengths, frequencies and photon energies of light of three different colours. In doing this you will develop some further practical skills, in particular, experimental design, taking measurements, estimating uncertainties, plotting graphs to illustrate these uncertainties using error bars, measuring gradients from graphs, combining equations to obtain a final result, and keeping a record of an experiment.

Activity 11.1   Investigating light

We expect this activity will take you approximately 2–3 hours.

The activity divides naturally into three parts, each of which requires about 40 minutes to an hour. You may split these three aspects of the work between different sessions; however, you may find it helpful to read through the whole activity first. You will do practical work only in Part 1 (Tasks 1 and 2) and Part 2 (Task 3).

Equipment (for Parts 1 and 2)

Diffraction grating (supplied in your Practical Kit)

Tungsten filament light bulb (40 W or 60 W) (see note below about light bulbs)

Energy-saving light bulb (see note below about light bulbs)

Anglepoise® lamp or table lamp

Cardboard box (e.g. breakfast cereal box) or piece of stiff cardboard

Some books, dark cloth or more cardboard to create a 'light-tight' enclosure

Modelling knife or sharp scissors to cut a narrow slit in the cardboard

Insulating tape or kitchen foil

Paper protractor (available on the course website or in the *Course Guide*) (Part 2 only)

Re-useable adhesive or modelling clay (e.g. Blu-Tack™ or Plasticene®) (Part 2 only)

About 50 cm of thread or thin string (preferably dark coloured) (Part 2 only)

A pin or needle (Part 2 only)

A drawing pin (Part 2 only)

Torch (Part 2 only)

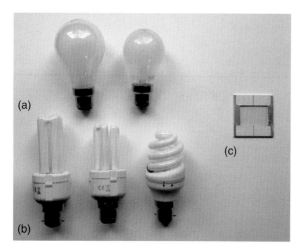

Figure 11.1   Some of the equipment used in Activity 11.1: (a) tungsten filament light bulbs; (b) energy-saving light bulbs; (c) the diffraction grating from the S104 Practical Kit. You will need just one light bulb of the type shown in (a) and one of the type shown in (b).

A note about light bulbs

Until recently, the vast majority of household light bulbs were tungsten filament light bulbs, producing visible light (and infrared radiation) from a tungsten filament at very high temperature (see Section 8.5). However, since about 2000, so-called 'energy-saving' light bulbs (also sometimes called 'eco bulbs') have become increasingly common. While being as bright as most conventional light bulbs, they consume typically less than 20% of the power, and last far longer. Not only do these bulbs save you money but, since they use far less power, you use less electricity, and so power stations release less greenhouse gases into the atmosphere. The environmental advantages of 'energy-saving' light bulbs have led several governments to decide to phase out conventional light bulbs.

For this experiment you will need to obtain an energy-saving light bulb, such as one of those shown in Figure 11.1b. You may already have an energy-saving light bulb in your home. If so, it is probably suitable for this activity. If not, suitable light bulbs can be readily obtained from electrical stores, supermarkets and the internet. If possible, you should also obtain a 40 W or 60 W tungsten filament light bulb (Figure 11.1a), for Task 1.

Aims

- To compare the spectrum produced by an energy-saving light bulb with that produced by a tungsten filament light bulb.
- To determine the wavelength, frequency and photon energy of light of three colours.

Introduction

In this experiment you will use a diffraction grating to examine the spectrum produced by an energy-saving light bulb. After making a qualitative description of the spectrum in Part 1, and comparing it with the spectrum of light from a tungsten filament light bulb, you will measure, in Part 2, the angles of diffraction for certain spectral lines that are present. In Part 3 you will use these angles of diffraction to determine the wavelength of the light corresponding to these lines. You will then convert these wavelengths into the corresponding frequencies, and finally into energies in electronvolts.

Tables have been provided for you to record your data, but you should also record how you did the experiment and any difficulties that arose. You should keep notes as you do the experiment, writing down anything that you think is important (do not be tempted to 'write it down later' – this is not good experimental practice). Include all of your results – don't be tempted to miss something out because you think that it is wrong. Also make a note of what you find difficult and what you think you could do better if you were to repeat the experiment. If an assignment question is set asking you to write up this experiment, you can base your report on the notes you make now.

Important safety precautions

Take note of the following safety precautions, which apply to all practical activities:

- Keep children and animals away while you are working.
- Clear your working area of clutter. Put all food away. Ensure there is nothing to trip on underfoot.
- Always wash your hands thoroughly after a practical activity.
- Any household items used should be thoroughly cleaned before returning them to domestic use.

In addition, you should note the following precautions which are specific to this activity:

- You will be using household light bulbs, which will become hot. Take care when handling the bulbs and do not allow them to come too close to cardboard or fabric, as this would be a fire risk.
- Take particular care when using your sharp knife or scissors to cut a slit in cardboard. Take care when handling pins, needles and drawing pins.
- You may be taking measurements in a darkened room. Take care not to trip over furniture or the lead for the lamp holding the light bulbs.

Part 1   Observing the diffraction patterns

The first part of this activity involves setting up the equipment and making some initial, qualitative observations of diffraction patterns.

You may like to glance through all the instructions before starting to set up your equipment.

Practical procedure

The first step is to gather together the equipment listed at the start of this activity.

This experiment is best done in a darkened room (total darkness is not necessary) and, ideally, on a steady surface, such as a large table, at least 1 m long. You will need about a metre of clear space at one end of the table to move around while taking measurements. You may want to protect the table with a cloth or cover.

An Anglepoise lamp is best for this activity as it allows greater flexibility, but a small table lamp is also adequate. The diffraction grating is shown in Figure 11.1c. The lines of the grating run parallel to its shorter side, and the line drawn on the slide mount is parallel to the grating lines. So the grating should be used with this line vertical.

Start by cutting a narrow, vertical slit near the bottom edge of the piece of cardboard. Ideally this should be about 50 mm long and about 0.5 to 1 mm wide, with sharp, straight edges. You could practise cutting this first with a spare piece of cardboard. If you have trouble cutting a slit that narrow, use two pieces of opaque tape (for instance insulating tape) stuck along the edges of a wider slit to reduce its width. Alternatively, you may be able to fold two pieces of kitchen foil over a wider slit to make it narrower and straight edged (Figure 11.2). The purpose of the slit is to restrict the size of the light source that you will observe through the diffraction grating. Be inventive!

Figure 11.2   Making the initial observations.

Insert the tungsten filament light bulb into the lamp and place the lamp at one end of the table. Arrange the lamp so that the bulb is no more than about 5 cm above the table surface. If you use an Anglepoise lamp, bend it down close to the table and point the bulb forwards so that it is parallel to the table surface. If you use a table lamp, you may find it easiest to remove the shade and stand the lamp on a chair just below the level of the table surface, so that the bulb just sticks up above the table. When you have the lamp in place, plug it in and switch on the power.

Next arrange the cardboard box or piece of card so that the slit is fixed *vertically* between you and the light source. Ensure that the card is not too close to the bulb or it may become hot – a distance of between 10 cm and 20 cm should be suitable. The bottom edge of the card should be in contact with the table so that no light passes underneath it.

It will certainly help if you can build a 'light-tight' housing around the sides and top of the lamp and slit arrangement. You could use more cardboard, books or a dark cloth for this purpose, but be careful to keep all such items at least 10 cm away from the bulb itself or they may become very hot. The only light you see should be that emerging through the slit. Stray light may lead to distractions and complications when taking the measurements. Again, be inventive!

Task 1 The diffraction pattern of a tungsten filament bulb

Having set up the equipment, squat down so that your eye line is level with the slit, and simply hold the diffraction grating up close to one eye (as shown in Figure 11.2). From a distance of about one metre, look through the grating towards the slit in the card and the light emerging through it. As you look through the grating, concentrate on the light that appears either side of the slit, and at the same height as the slit (any other light you see will be due to leakage).

Make a few notes describing what you can see as you look through the grating towards the slit. A sketch may help you to illustrate some of the features. You could comment on the following questions.

- How many orders of the diffraction pattern are visible? *2 orders.*
- Is the pattern identical to the left and right of the centre? *Yes*
- How are the colours distributed within each diffraction order? *bands of color full range of Visible Spectrum*
- Is the spectrum the same for each order that you can see? *2nd order band wider distributed.*
- What does the zero order, in the centre of the pattern, look like? *White light.*

Now switch off the power to the lamp and wait for the bulb to cool down for a few minutes.

Look at the comments on Task 1 at the end of this book before continuing.

Task 2 The diffraction pattern of an energy-saving bulb

Replace the tungsten filament light bulb with the energy-saving bulb. (Be careful handling the tungsten filament bulb if it is still hot.) Examine closely the spectrum of this new light source, as you did for the tungsten bulb.

Make a few notes describing what you can see as you look through the grating towards the slit. As in Task 1, a sketch may help, and you could comment on the following questions.

2nd   1st
red,   uv   red ← uv

- How many orders of the diffraction pattern are visible? *2*
- Is the pattern identical to the left and right of the centre? *Yes*
- What features can you see within each order of the diffraction pattern? How are the colours distributed? *tight seperate bands of color rather than merged like above*
- Is the spectrum the same for each order that you can see? *Wider distribution of 2nd order 135 like above.*
- What does the zero order, in the centre of the pattern, look like? *White light*

Before you move on to the next part of this activity, look at the comments on Task 2 at the end of this book and then try to answer the following questions to consolidate your understanding of these spectra.

Question 11.1

(a) How do the spectra of the two bulbs differ from the spectra of the lasers that you saw being used in Activity 9.1?

(b) What terms would you use to describe the types of spectra produced by each type of light bulb?

Full spectrum of colours rather than dots.
bands rather than dots

Continuos spectra
emission spectra (line spectra)

Question 11.2

From what you have seen of the spectra of tungsten filament light bulbs and energy-saving light bulbs (both here and in Section 8.5), why are the latter more energy efficient?

Part 2 of this activity involves taking measurements of the spectrum of the energy-saving light bulb. If you are going to do Part 2 now, leave the equipment set up. However, if you plan to do it another time, bear in mind that you will need to use all the equipment again in Part 2.

Part 2 Measuring diffraction angles

In this part of the investigation you will determine the wavelengths of the various lines in the spectrum of the energy-saving light bulb. To do this you need to devise a means of measuring the angle of diffraction of each spectral line, in each order of the diffraction pattern. You may like to consider for yourself how you could do this. One suggestion is made below but you may prefer to devise your own method.

Practical procedure

If necessary, set up the equipment again as you did for Part 1 and, if you don't already have them, gather together the additional pieces of equipment needed for Part 2. A paper protractor with an angular scale marked in degrees is provided. Either print it out from the course website or cut out the copy in the *Course Guide*.

Figure 11.3 illustrates one method for determining the angles of diffraction. If you use this method, you should proceed as follows.

Push a drawing pin from the back of the paper through the axis of the paper protractor (the point where all the lines converge, marked by a dot) and then stick the paper protractor to the table using tape or re-useable adhesive. The head of the drawing pin should be in contact with the table, with the point sticking up through the paper, and the paper protractor should be between 50 cm and 1 m away from the lamp and slit. Make sure that the flat edge of the protractor is closest to, and parallel to, the piece of card that contains the slit, and that the zero degree line of the protractor is pointing directly towards the slit (Figure 11.3).

Next fasten a length of thread or thin string to the drawing pin; about 50 cm should be sufficient. Dark-coloured thread will probably show up best against the white paper of the protractor.

There is a line drawn on the diffraction grating marking an axis through its centre. Make sure that this line is facing you and, using re-useable adhesive or

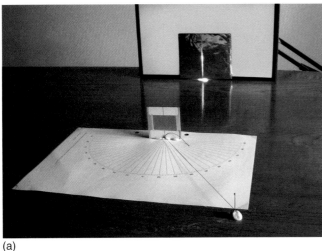 

(a)   (b)

Figure 11.3   One possible method of measuring the angle of diffraction of each spectral line: (a) the experimental arrangement; (b) the experiment in progress.

modelling clay, mount the diffraction grating along the flat edge of the protractor, so that the line is vertical and is as close as possible to the drawing pin which marks the protractor's axis.

The protractor and grating should remain fixed in position throughout the experiment once everything is aligned correctly.

Finally, tie a pin or needle to the free end of the thread. Stick the end of the pin in a piece of re-useable adhesive or modelling clay, to make it easier to hold.

Now, when you look through the grating towards the slit, and move your head from side to side, you will see the bright lines in the spectrum of the energy-saving bulb. In Task 3 you will be asked to determine the angle of diffraction for particular lines. To try out this procedure you should move your head from side to side and at the same time find a position for the pin or needle that allows you to line up a spectral line, the line drawn on the diffraction grating, and the pin or needle at the end of the thread. You will have to close one eye for this (to avoid so-called parallax effects) and should make sure that the thread remains taut. You may find this easier with one eye than the other. When you have achieved this alignment, the thread will register the angle of diffraction θ_n on the scale of the protractor.

Remember that an angle of diffraction of zero degrees corresponds to the straight-through position, and so should correspond to the position of the zero order – the slit itself. Make sure that the slit does indeed correspond to an angle of zero degrees on the protractor. If it does not, adjust the position of the card containing the slit until it does.

The aim of this experiment is to determine the wavelengths of several spectral lines. As noted in the comments on Task 2, you should be able to see three or possibly four orders of the spectrum on either side of the central position, but the lines may well be brighter on one side than the other. Within each order you can probably see at least four or five reasonably bright emission lines along with many fainter ones. The brightest are probably the blue, green and red lines.

You can, of course, measure angles of diffraction for spectral lines to the left *and* right of the centre of the pattern and these angles should be equal. For instance, the angle of diffraction of the green line in the second order spectrum to the left of the centre should be the same as the angle of diffraction of the green line in the second order spectrum to the right of the centre.

Each of your measurements of θ_n will have an associated experimental uncertainty (Book 1, Sections 3.1.2 and 3.1.3). The paper protractor only registers angular divisions of a degree, but you may be able to estimate angles to the nearest half-degree. There is an additional uncertainty associated with the difficulty in lining up the pin with the mark on the grating and the spectral line. For the fainter or more diffuse lines the uncertainty in your measurements may well be larger than for those lines that are brighter, or more sharply defined. Make a note of the sources of uncertainty in your experimental set-up including quantitative estimates of the size of the uncertainties.

Task 3 Measuring angles of diffraction

Bearing in mind the general comments above, measure the angles of diffraction of the blue, green and red lines in each of the first, second and third order spectra in the diffraction pattern (and the fourth order if you can see it) and record the angles in Table 11.1. You may find it helpful to use a torch when taking and recording the measurements, particularly if you have blacked out all other light sources. Remember, for each angle, include an estimate of the measurement uncertainty. To save time, you should measure the angles on just one side of the zero order (either to the right or to the left, whichever is brighter). However, you may wish to check quickly, for one or two lines, that the angles are similar on each side of the pattern. You may also want to repeat some measurements to help you to estimate the uncertainty in each angle (see Book 1, Section 3.1.3).

Table 11.1 For use in Task 3 to record angular measurements and the last two columns are used in Task 4.

Order, n	θ_n/degrees	Uncertainty in θ_n/degrees	$\sin \theta_n$	Uncertainty in $\sin \theta_n$
blue spectral line				
1	6.5	±1.0	0.12 ~~0.113~~	±0.03
2	15.5	±1.5	0.27 ~~0.271~~	±0.05 Smaller
3	22	±2.0	0.38 ~~0.385~~	±0.07 ↓
4				
green spectral line				
1	9	±1.0	0.16 ~~0.156~~	±0.03
2	~~20~~ 19	±1.5	0.33 ~~0.326~~	±0.05 Smaller
3	29	±2.0	0.49 ~~0.485~~	±0.07 ↓
4				
red spectral line				
1	10	±1.0	0.18 ~~0.174~~	±0.03
2	~~20~~ 21	±1.5	0.36 ~~0.358~~	±0.05 Smaller
3	33	±2.0	0.55 ~~0.545~~	±0.05 ↓
4				

Having determined the value of θ_n for the different orders n for each of three spectral lines, you can now proceed to calculate the wavelengths of these lines.

First you may want to check your values for the diffraction angles against the values in the comments on the task at the end of this book. If you need to repeat any measurements you should do so now, otherwise you may want to pack away the equipment and find somewhere more convenient to complete this work.

Part 3   Determining the photon energies of the spectral lines

The final part of this activity involves analysing the results you have just obtained.

Determining the wavelength

The stages in determining the wavelengths of each spectral line are:

- to calculate values for sin θ_n corresponding to each diffraction angle that you measured in Part 2
- to plot graphs of sin θ_n against n to find the best-fit straight line through the data
- to measure the gradient of each graph and so calculate the wavelength of each spectral line.

Task 4   Calculating sin θ_n

For each value of θ_n that you have measured for each spectral line, calculate sin θ_n. Write these values in the fourth column of Table 11.1, quoting them to two significant figures in each case.

To take account of the uncertainty in your measured angles, be sure to calculate a range of values for sin θ_n in each case. For example, if you measured a certain angle to be $\theta_n = 15° \pm 1°$, the maximum value of sin θ_n that is consistent with your measurement is sin $16° = 0.28$, and the minimum value of sin θ_n that is consistent with your measurement is sin $14° = 0.24$. Since sin $15° = 0.26$, the value of sin θ_n that you would record in the table is 0.26 and the uncertainty in sin θ_n is ± 0.02 in this case.

For some angles, the upper limit of sin θ_n may not be the same distance from the middle value as the lower limit of sin θ_n. For instance, if $\theta_n = 41° \pm 2°$, the middle value for the sine of the angle is 0.66, and the upper and lower limits are 0.68 and 0.63, respectively. In this case, it is probably best to overestimate the total uncertainty and to express the result as 0.66 ± 0.03. Write the uncertainties in each value of sin θ_n in the fifth column of Table 11.1.

Now check your values against those in the comments for Task 4 at the end of this book before continuing with the activity.

Task 5   Plotting graphs with error bars

Now, plot a graph on Figure 11.4 for each of the three sets of results that you have obtained. These can all go on the same set of axes for convenience. As in Activity 9.2, it is conventional to plot the measured (dependent) variable, in this case sin θ_n, up the vertical axis of the graph, and the independent variable, in this case n, along the horizontal axis.

Uncertainties can be expressed on a graph by drawing what is known as an **error bar** at each point. An error bar represents the full range of a value that is consistent with what is measured. For example, if you have recorded a particular

Figure 11.4   Graph paper for Task 5 of Activity 11.1.

value as sin $\theta_n = 0.13 \pm 0.02$, you would plot it as shown in Figure 11.5. The error bar extends from sin $\theta_n = 0.13 - 0.02 = 0.11$ up to $0.13 + 0.02 = 0.15$. It shows that the true value of sin θ_n could be anywhere within this range. Plot error bars for each of your measured values.

There is an extra point which you can plot for each set of data. Remember that the zero order of the diffraction pattern is coincident with the bright, white vertical line in the centre of the pattern – the slit in the card. All light, whatever its wavelength, appears at this same position in the pattern. The angle of diffraction of the zero order is $0°$ and sin $0° = 0$. So on your graph the point where $n = 0$ and sin $\theta_n = 0$ should also be plotted.

Consider whether the point at the origin should also have an error bar. You could only set the apparatus up so that the zero order was at zero degrees to the precision with which you could measure angles. So the angle of diffraction for the zero order will have an associated uncertainty of about the same size as those of other measured positions. You can therefore draw an error bar for the zero order point that is similar in size to those on your other data points.

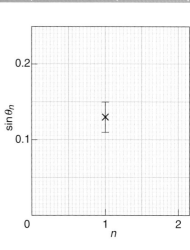

Figure 11.5 The error bar for the result sin $\theta_n = 0.13 \pm 0.02$ at $n = 1$. The point in the centre of the error bar corresponds to the measured value, in this case, $n = 1$, sin $\theta_n = 0.13$. The vertical line stretches from sin $\theta_n = 0.11$ to sin $\theta_n = 0.15$, corresponding to the range of values consistent with the measurement.

Task 6 The best-fit straight line for a set of data points

Once you have plotted the graphs for each spectral line, draw what you consider to be the best-fit straight line through the data. Remember that the error bars indicate the possible range of a measurement – the true value may lie anywhere within the length of the error bar. So the best-fit straight line need not pass through the centre of every error bar, but it should pass through some part of each one.

■ If the best-fit straight line for a set of data passes close to the centre of every error bar on a graph, as in Figure 11.6a, what might this indicate?

☐ This might indicate that the experimental uncertainties were overestimated, and the true error bars should be somewhat smaller. The experimenter in this case has been rather pessimistic.

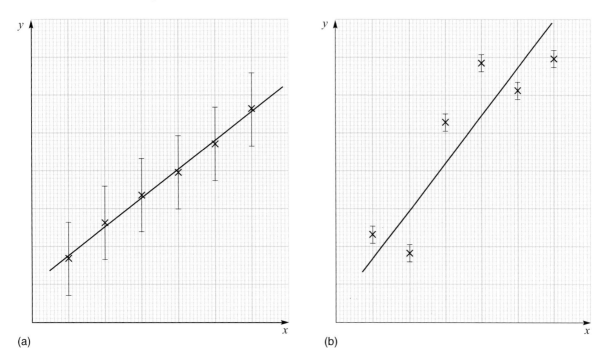

(a)   (b)

Figure 11.6 An example of (a) overestimated error bars and (b) underestimated error bars.

■ If the best-fit straight line for a set of data does not pass through any of the error bars on a graph, as in Figure 11.6b, what might this indicate?

☐ This might indicate that the experimental uncertainties were underestimated, and the true error bars should be larger. Here the experimenter has been rather optimistic.

Now look at the comments for Tasks 5 and 6 at the end of this book before continuing with the activity.

Task 7 The gradient of the straight lines

The final stage in determining the wavelengths of the spectral lines is to measure the gradients of the three graphs that you have just plotted. As you saw in Activity 9.2, the gradient of a graph of $\sin \theta_n$ against n is simply $\dfrac{\lambda}{d}$. The grating you have used in Activity 11.1 has 300 lines per mm, so:

$$d = \frac{1}{300 \text{ mm}^{-1}} = 3.33 \times 10^{-3} \text{ mm or } 3.33 \times 10^{-6} \text{ m}$$

Measure the gradient of each graph and so calculate the wavelength of each spectral line that you measured.

Look at the comments for Task 7 at the end of this book before continuing with the activity.

■ To determine the wavelengths of the red, green and blue spectral lines produced by the energy-saving bulb, you measured the angles of diffraction for each line in each order of the diffraction pattern. What is the advantage of this technique over taking a single angular measurement in a single order of the diffraction pattern and then calculating the wavelength of each line directly using $\lambda = \dfrac{d \sin \theta_n}{n}$?

☐ Taking just a single measurement of the angle of diffraction may lead to the possibility of a significant error in the measurement. This could arise simply through a measuring mistake for instance. By taking angular measurements in each order of the diffraction pattern, and then plotting a graph of the results, the effect of this source of error is reduced. You will also note if one point is badly out of line with the others. The values you have obtained for the wavelengths of the spectral lines are derived from an average of all the measurements that you took, and a single discrepant result therefore has less effect on the final values.

Also, by plotting the uncertainty in each measurement as an error bar on the graph, you can take account of the uncertainties in a simple way when drawing the best-fit straight line. In general, in any practical work, taking several measurements and determining values graphically, so averaging over all readings, is preferable to taking just a single measurement.

Determining the frequency and photon energy

You have now determined the wavelength of three spectral lines in the spectrum produced by an energy-saving light bulb. The final step is to relate these wavelengths to the energy carried by the photons.

Task 8   Converting wavelengths into frequencies

Using Equation 9.2, $c = f\lambda$, calculate the frequency corresponding to each of the wavelengths that you have calculated. (Assume that $c = 3.00 \times 10^8$ m s^{-1}.)

Task 9   Converting frequencies into energies

Using Equation 10.1, $E_{ph} = hf$, calculate the energy, in electronvolts, corresponding to each of the frequencies that you have just calculated. (Assume that $h = 4.14 \times 10^{-15}$ eV Hz^{-1}.)

Now look at the comments for Tasks 8 and 9 at the end of this book before continuing with the activity.

Task 10   Discussion of Activity 11.1

Energy-saving light bulbs contain mercury vapour which emits light as an emission line spectrum with wavelengths of 405 nm (violet), 436 nm (blue), 546 nm (green), 578 nm (yellow) and 618 nm (red). In addition, the ultraviolet part of the mercury spectrum (mainly at a wavelength of 254 nm) is converted into visible light by a thin layer of fluorescent powder on the inside of the glass tube. The powders used vary depending on the type of bulb, so bulbs whose colour is described as 'warm white' use different powders than those whose colour is described as 'cool white'. However, the powders are chosen so as to produce spectral lines whose colours complement those of the mercury vapour and span the whole of the visible light range. In this way, the light output of the bulb appears as white rather than any particular colour.

The lines you measured in the spectrum of the energy-saving light bulb were the bright blue, green and red lines. These lines have wavelengths of 436 nm, 542–546 nm and 618 nm, respectively. The wavelength values that you have calculated from your own measurements will probably lie within about 50 nm of these values. The equivalent photon energies, corresponding to radiation of these wavelengths, are 2.84 eV, 2.28 eV and 2.01 eV, respectively. Your calculated values will probably lie within about 0.2 eV of these values.

In Book 7 you will learn that the energy carried by photons originates in energy changes taking place within the atoms of which all matter is composed. So, in Activity 11.1 – and using only a light bulb and a diffraction grating – you have discovered something about the energy changes in mercury atoms. You will discover more about the significance of this in Book 7.

The experiment that you have just completed is the longest and most complicated piece of practical work you will be asked to do in this course, so pause for a moment to reflect on what you have achieved. To summarise what you did:

- You measured the angles at which certain spectral lines (different colours) were diffracted by a grating.
- You then plotted graphs of $\sin \theta_n$ against n for each coloured line, and so determined the wavelength from the gradient using Equation 9.4,
$$\sin \theta_n = \frac{n\lambda}{d}.$$
- Using Equation 9.2, $c = f\lambda$, you converted these wavelengths into frequencies.
- Using Equation 10.1, $E_{ph} = hf$, you converted these frequencies into photon energies.

We hope that your results were reasonably close to those given above. Remember that the equipment that you used was not very sophisticated and there will have been several contributing uncertainties. More importantly, Activity 11.1 provided an opportunity for you to practise many of the skills developed in Book 3. You will be encouraged to reflect on your achievements in these new skills in Activity 12.1.

There are no further comments on this activity.

11.2   Matter as particles and waves

You have seen in this book that light, which propagates as if it is a wave, interacts as if it is composed of a stream of particles called photons. You may be wondering, therefore, whether matter, which is normally thought of as being composed of particles, propagates like a wave. Well, if you are wondering this then congratulate yourself because, 80 years ago, such thoughts could have set you on course for a Nobel Prize in Physics! The idea that objects such as electrons, which are usually thought of as particles, can exhibit wave-like properties was first suggested in 1923 by Louis de Broglie (pronounced 'de Broy') (see Figure 11.7).

Clearly, this is a very strange concept. After all, light obviously differs from matter – the nature of light can be determined only by indirect observations such as diffraction and the photoelectric effect, whereas material objects can usually be seen. You can see that a handful of salt is made of individual grains and in everyday experience salt does not exhibit any wave-like properties. But, as you will discover as you study the rest of this course, salt grains are crystals of sodium chloride, which in turn are composed of ions of sodium and chlorine, which in turn are composed of electrons, protons and neutrons, and the protons and neutrons are composed of fundamental particles called quarks – none of which can be seen directly any more than light waves or photons can. When talking about the wave-like behaviour of particles, it is these smallest components that are relevant.

If particles, such as electrons, propagate as though they are waves, they should exhibit wave-like behaviour. The crucial property that demonstrates wave-like behaviour is diffraction. So, can a beam of electrons be diffracted? Well, yes it can, provided an object is used that has a sufficiently small 'aperture' for the electrons to be diffracted through. The apertures in ordinary diffraction gratings are simply too large to cause any noticeable diffraction to occur with a beam of electrons. However, a beam of electrons may be diffracted using many substances that possess a crystal structure, i.e. the ions of which they are composed lie in regularly spaced planes. The spacings between these planes have a somewhat similar effect to the slits in a diffraction grating but the planes have a much smaller spacing – typically a few nanometres.

Remember what was said earlier about the conditions necessary for diffraction to occur – the apertures must be of similar size to the wavelength of the waves concerned. This implies that the wavelength of a beam of electrons must be around a nanometre if it is to be diffracted by a crystal. The wavelength of an electron beam is determined by the energy of the electrons.

Figure 11.7   Louis Victor, 7th duc de Broglie (France) (1892–1987), was the first person to propose that particles can, in some circumstances, behave as waves. He was influenced by Einstein's work on the photoelectric effect and, in 1923, suggested that particles, such as electrons, might behave as waves, and could be diffracted. Not many of his colleagues took these ideas seriously but Einstein enthusiastically advocated that they be tested experimentally. Within four years, electron diffraction patterns had been produced, proving that de Broglie was correct.

■ What type of electromagnetic radiation would you expect to be diffracted by apertures whose size is a few nanometres?

☐ X-rays have wavelengths of around a nanometre (Figure 9.10), so they should also be diffracted by the same structures that diffract electrons.

This is illustrated in Figure 11.8 which shows examples of electron and X-ray diffraction patterns.

You may now be wondering, why can't diffraction effects be detected with everyday objects? The reason is that everyday objects, when moving, have a large amount of energy, and the larger the energy of an object, the smaller its wavelength. For this reason, you are not noticeably diffracted when you pass through a doorway – your wavelength is simply too small compared with the width of the doorway.

You will return to the study of the wave–particle duality of matter in Book 7, when you will discover that this is one aspect of the weird – but extremely successful – science of quantum mechanics.

11.3   Summary of Chapter 11

Light always propagates like a wave and always interacts like a beam of particles, called photons. In truth it is neither a wave nor a particle but it is convenient to describe its behaviour in terms of one or the other, as the situation requires.

Just as electromagnetic radiation interacts with matter as though it were a stream of particles, so electrons propagate as though they were a wave. This is illustrated by the fact that a beam of electrons can be diffracted by the closely packed planes of ions in a crystal.

The wavelength of a beam of electrons is typically less than 1 nm and decreases as the electron energy is increased.

In studying this chapter you have carried out an experiment that relies on both the wave-like propagation and the particle-like interaction of light. You have taken measurements and considered experimental design and uncertainties. You have plotted graphs, found their gradients, related the gradients to the equation of a straight line and combined equations in order to obtain your final results.

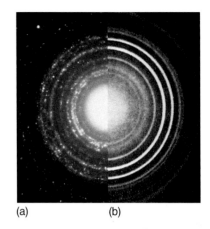

(a)   (b)

Figure 11.8   Photographs of diffraction patterns obtained with a target made of zirconium oxide: (a) using a beam of electrons and (b) using X-rays (electromagnetic radiation). The wavelength of the electron beam was set to be the same as the wavelength of X-rays. Because the zirconium and oxygen atoms in the crystal form a three-dimensional structure, the diffraction pattern is more complex than those produced using the simple (one-dimensional) diffraction gratings that you saw earlier.

Chapter 12
Summary of Book 3

Just remember that you're standing on a planet that's evolving and revolving at 900 miles an hour;

That's orbiting at 19 miles a second, so it's reckoned, a sun that is the source of all our power …

Eric Idle, *The Galaxy Song* (from Monty Python's *The Meaning of Life*, 1983)

In Book 3 you have considered the way in which energy is transferred from one object to another and transformed from one type to another, thus enabling all of the movement observed on Earth and in the wider Solar System, from planets orbiting, to continents drifting, to cheetahs chasing their prey and insects scurrying about in the undergrowth. Human society relies heavily (many people would say too heavily) on energy; the burning of fossil fuels to power factories, cars, aeroplanes and homes is one of the factors blamed for global warming, as you learned in Book 1.

Energy is ultimately conserved but it can take many different forms and be classified in many different ways. You have considered kinetic energy, potential energy, internal energy and electrical energy in some detail in this book and you have learned how energy is related to force, work, power, heat and temperature. Einstein's remarkable equation $E = mc^2$ is a reminder that mass, the very stuff of matter, can also be considered a form of energy. Nuclear fusion, the Sun's energy source, relies on this and so does nuclear fission, the process that drives nuclear power stations on Earth.

Energy is transported from the Sun to the Earth by means of visible light and other forms of electromagnetic radiation. Visible light is very familiar and other forms of electromagnetic radiation are used every time you switch on a microwave oven, watch the television, use a mobile phone or have an X-ray in hospital or at the dentist. Electromagnetic radiation is well understood by scientists, yet it has a rather strange property – in order to describe all its properties, it must sometimes be considered as a wave and sometimes as a particle. You have considered both the wave-like properties (especially diffraction) and the particle-like properties (needed to explain the photoelectric effect) in this book.

In exploring the science of energy and light, this book has introduced you to the scientific discipline usually called physics. In addition, you have encountered a large range of important scientific skills, most of which you will use for the rest of the course. In particular, you have developed the mathematical skills of rearranging and combining equations as well as skills associated with problem solving. You have also revised skills associated with handling units and significant figures in calculations and have developed previously introduced skills associated with interpreting the gradient of a straight-line graph. You have completed two activities involving practical work and so developed the important practical work skills of measuring, recording and analysing as well as the communication skill of writing a report on an experiment you have done. Activity 12.1 will help you to monitor your progress towards the course learning outcomes associated with these skills.

Activity 12.1 Your progress towards the course learning outcomes

We expect this activity will take you approximately 15 minutes.

At the end of Books 1 and 2 you were encouraged to monitor your progress towards the course learning outcomes. In Book 3 you have made very rapid progress towards specific learning outcomes, especially the cognitive skill of addressing problems, several key mathematical skills and the practical skills of making and recording observations and measurements and reporting results.

Look at Table 12.1. It lists, in more detail than the list of course learning outcomes in the *Course Guide*, the mathematical, problem-solving and practical skills developed in Book 3. You may be amazed by just how much you have learned! (And this is just in these specific areas – you have learned other things too.) However, you might have found some of the maths or practical work difficult. The purpose of this activity is to help you identify any areas that are causing you problems.

Tick the appropriate cell in each row of Table 12.1 to rate your ability in each skill. In judging your ability, you could think about whether you were able to complete the activities and questions in this book. It doesn't matter if you couldn't do them to start with, or if you found them difficult – did you get there in the end? Also, how well did you get on with the relevant assessment questions?

An electronic copy of Table 12.1 is available for downloading from the course website and you are advised to complete this version if possible, so that you can store it with other records of your study progress.

The comments on this activity at the end of this book give some suggestions for what to do if you feel you need more practice at any of these skills.

Table 12.1 Skills developed or practised in Book 3.

Skill	Very confident	Confident	Fairly confident	Still struggling	Having real difficulty
Using symbols for quantities and units					
Rearranging equations					
Solving problems					
Working out the units					
Significant figures					
Combining equations					
Proportionality					
Plotting graphs					
Drawing best-fit straight lines					
Calculating the gradient of a straight-line graph					
Relating the gradient of a graph to the equation of a straight line					
Finding the sine of an angle					
Following the instructions for practical work					
Setting up experiments					
Observing experimental results					
Taking measurements					
Estimating uncertainties					
Keeping a record of an experiment					
Calculating the results of an experiment					
Writing a report on experimental work					

The skills developed in Book 3 and your understanding of the scientific principles of energy conversion and conservation mean that you are in a good position to continue your exploration of science. However, you won't be leaving the world of energy behind; for example, you will consider the energy transformations in chemical reactions in Book 4 and the energy flow through ecosystems in Book 5.

You have encountered atoms and molecules several times already; in Book 1 you learned that the properties of greenhouse gases can be explained in terms of their molecular structure; in Book 3 you considered the importance, for internal energy, of the movement of molecules and the electrical forces between atoms. In Book 3, you also discovered the importance of the subatomic particles known as electrons in the conduction of electricity, and you were introduced to the idea that nuclear fission and nuclear fusion depend on changes taking place deep within the atom, in the nuclei. You will learn more about this in Book 7. In Book 7 you will also return to the mysterious world of wave–particle duality (of both light and matter) and quantum mechanics. However, all of this requires a more detailed understanding of the structure of molecules and atoms. Book 4 *The Right Chemistry* will give you this.

Answers to questions

Comments on the answers are given in square brackets […].

Question 2.1

(a) As the ball falls, gravitational potential energy is converted into kinetic energy.

When the ball reaches the ground, the ball is deformed (squashed) and so the kinetic energy is converted into strain potential energy.

As the ball regains its normal shape, the strain potential energy is converted back to kinetic energy; then, as the ball rises, the kinetic energy is converted into gravitational potential energy. At the top of the bounce the ball temporarily stops moving so it has no kinetic energy at this point, and a maximum of gravitational potential energy. The process is then repeated.

Each time the ball hits the ground, some energy is converted into sound energy and heat energy, so there is less and less kinetic energy available to convert to gravitational potential energy on each subsequent bounce, so the height to which the ball rises gradually diminishes and the ball eventually stops bouncing altogether.

(b) The energy of the wind (a form of kinetic energy) causes the blades of the wind turbine to rotate (another form of kinetic energy) and this kinetic energy is converted into electrical energy. The electrical energy is converted into light energy in the light bulb. The way in which this happens depends on the type of light bulb, as you will discover in Activity 11.1 near the end of this book.

(c) As the archer draws back the bow, chemical energy in her arm is transferred to strain potential energy in the bow, and then to kinetic energy in the arrow.

Experienced archers shoot arrows slightly upwards, so there is a loss of kinetic energy and a gain of gravitational potential energy as the arrow gains in height, then a loss of gravitational potential energy and a corresponding gain in kinetic energy as the arrow approaches the target.

As the arrow moves through the air, some of its kinetic energy will be converted into internal energy of the air (i.e. kinetic energy of the air molecules). This is the cause of air resistance.

As the arrow hits the target, the kinetic energy in the arrow is transferred to strain potential energy in the target and to sound. There is likely to be a very small increase in internal energy (heat) in the target too.

Question 3.1

(a) The kinetic energy of the athlete is as follows.

$$E_k = \frac{1}{2}mv^2$$

$$= \frac{1}{2} \times (75 \text{ kg}) \times (8.5 \text{ m s}^{-1})^2$$

$$= 2.7 \times 10^3 \text{ kg m}^2 \text{ s}^{-2}$$

$$= 2.7 \times 10^3 \text{ J to two significant figures}$$

(b) The kinetic energy of the lithospheric plate is as follows.

$$E_k = \frac{1}{2}mv^2$$

$$= \frac{1}{2} \times (4.0 \times 10^{21} \text{ kg}) \times (1.0 \times 10^{-9} \text{ m s}^{-1})^2$$

$$= 2.0 \times 10^3 \text{ kg m}^2 \text{ s}^{-2}$$

$$= 2.0 \times 10^3 \text{ J to two significant figures}$$

[Comparing the answers to (a) and (b) shows that the athlete has a larger kinetic energy. This may surprise you, given the lithospheric plate's huge mass. However, it is another demonstration of the importance of speed, the squared term in Equation 3.1.]

Question 3.2

(a) $v = f\lambda$ can be reversed to give $f\lambda = v$.

To isolate f you need to remove λ, and f is currently *multiplied* by λ so, according to Hint 3, you need to *divide* by λ. Remember that you must do this to both sides of the equation, so you have:

$$\frac{f\lambda}{\lambda} = \frac{v}{\lambda}$$

The λ in the numerator (top line) of the fraction on the left-hand side cancels with the λ in the denominator (bottom line) to give:

$$f = \frac{v}{\lambda}$$

(b) $E_{tot} = E_k + E_g$ can be reversed to give $E_k + E_g = E_{tot}$.

To isolate E_k you need to remove E_g, and E_g is currently *added* to E_k so, according to Hint 1, you need to *subtract* E_g. Remember that you must do this to both sides of the equation, so you have:

$$E_k + E_g - E_g = E_{tot} - E_g$$

so

$$E_k = E_{tot} - E_g \quad (\text{since } E_g - E_g = 0)$$

(c) $I = \frac{Q}{t}$ can be reversed to give $\frac{Q}{t} = I$.

To isolate Q you need to remove t, and Q is currently *divided* by t so, according to Hint 4, you need to *multiply* by t. Remember that you must do this to both sides of the equation, so you have:

$$\frac{Qt}{t} = It$$

The t in the numerator of the fraction on the left-hand side cancels with the t in the denominator to give:

$$Q = It$$

Question 3.3

(a) $E = mc^2$ can be reversed to give $mc^2 = E$.

Dividing both sides by m gives:

$$\frac{mc^2}{m} = \frac{E}{m}$$

Cancelling the m terms on the left-hand side gives:

$$c^2 = \frac{E}{m}$$

Taking the square root of both sides gives:

$$c = \sqrt{\frac{E}{m}}$$

(b) Multiplying both sides of $\rho = \dfrac{m}{V}$ by V gives:

$$\rho V = \frac{mV}{V}$$

Cancelling the V terms on the right-hand side gives:

$$\rho V = m$$

Since you want an equation for V, you now need to remove the ρ on the left-hand side by dividing both sides by ρ:

$$\frac{\rho V}{\rho} = \frac{m}{\rho}$$

Cancelling the ρ terms on the left-hand side gives:

$$V = \frac{m}{\rho}$$

(c) Note that in the equation $a = \dfrac{v - u}{t}$, the whole of $(v - u)$ is divided by t. You may find it helpful to write the equation as $a = \dfrac{(v - u)}{t}$. This can be reversed to give:

$$\frac{(v - u)}{t} = a$$

Multiplying both sides by t gives:

$$\frac{(v - u) \times t}{t} = at$$

Cancelling the t terms on the left-hand side gives:

$$v - u = at$$

Adding u to both sides gives:

$$v - u + u = at + u$$

i.e.

$$v = at + u$$

Question 3.4

(a) $E_k = \frac{1}{2}mv^2$ (Equation 3.1) can be reversed to give:

$$\frac{1}{2}mv^2 = E_k$$

Multiplying both sides by 2 gives:

$$2 \times \frac{1}{2}mv^2 = 2E_k$$

that is:

$$mv^2 = 2E_k$$

Dividing both sides by v^2 gives:

$$\frac{mv^2}{v^2} = \frac{2E_k}{v^2}$$

The v^2 terms on the left-hand side cancel to give:

$$m = \frac{2E_k}{v^2}$$

(b) Substituting values of $E_k = 1.0 \times 10^{-3}$ J and $v = 4.5$ m s^{-1} into $m = \dfrac{2E_k}{v^2}$ gives:

$$
\begin{aligned}
m &= \frac{2E_k}{v^2} \\[6pt]
&= \frac{2 \times 1.0 \times 10^{-3} \text{ J}}{(4.5 \text{ m s}^{-1})^2} \\[6pt]
&= \frac{2 \times 1.0 \times 10^{-3} \text{ kg m}^2 \text{ s}^{-2}}{4.5^2 \text{ m}^2 \text{ s}^{-2}} \\[6pt]
&= 9.9 \times 10^{-5} \text{ kg to two significant figures}
\end{aligned}
$$

Note that the units of m^2 s^{-2} cancel on the right-hand side of the equation.

The mass of the bee is just less than 1×10^{-4} kg, which is 0.1 g.

Question 4.1

Using Equation 4.8, $W = Fd$ and substituting $F = 1.9 \times 10^3$ N and $d = 6.5$ m gives:

$$W = Fd$$

$$= 1.9 \times 10^3 \text{ N} \times 6.5 \text{ m}$$

$$= 1.235 \times 10^4 \text{ N m}$$

$$= 1.2 \times 10^4 \text{ N m to two significant figures}$$

However, 1 N m = 1 J (Equation 4.9) so the work done on the piano is 1.2×10^4 J.

Question 4.2

You need to find d, so you should start by rearranging $W = Fd$ to make d the subject. Reversing the equation gives:

$$Fd = W$$

Dividing both sides by F gives:

$$\frac{Fd}{F} = \frac{W}{F}$$

The F terms on the left-hand side cancel to give:

$$d = \frac{W}{F}$$

You can then substitute $W = 2.8 \times 10^2$ J and $F = 2.79 \times 10^4$ N, remembering that 1 J = 1 N m, so:

$$d = \frac{W}{F}$$

$$= \frac{2.8 \times 10^2 \text{ J}}{2.79 \times 10^4 \text{ N}}$$

$$= \frac{2.8 \times 10^2 \text{ N m}}{2.79 \times 10^4 \text{ N}}$$

$$= 1.004 \times 10^{-2} \text{ m}$$

W was given to two significant figures and F was given to three significant figures so, following the advice in Book 1, Section 3.1.4, the answer should be given to two significant figures. So the platform was raised a distance of $d = 1.0 \times 10^{-2}$ m or 1.0 cm.

[Note that the units of N cancelled to give final units of m. Note also that you didn't need to use the value of the mass quoted in the question. Finally, note the (relatively!) small amount of work involved in lifting this enormous mass a small distance.]

Question 4.3

If $m = 0.20$ kg, $u = 1.0$ m s^{-1} and $v = 2.0$ m s^{-1}, substituting in Equation 4.11 gives:

$$W = \Delta E_k$$

$$= \frac{1}{2}mv^2 - \frac{1}{2}mu^2$$

$$= \left[\frac{1}{2} \times 0.20 \text{ kg} \times (2.0 \text{ m s}^{-1})^2\right] - \left[\frac{1}{2} \times 0.20 \text{ kg} \times (1.0 \text{ m s}^{-1})^2\right]$$

$$= 0.40 \text{ J} - 0.10 \text{ J}$$

$$= 0.30 \text{ J to two significant figures}$$

The work done on the toy train is 0.30 J.

Question 4.4

If there is friction within the train mechanism, there will be a continual conversion of kinetic energy into internal energy. This means that the kinetic energy of the train will decrease steadily until it is zero, so the speed of the train will decrease, and the train will eventually stop.

Question 4.5

You need to rearrange $P = \dfrac{E}{t}$ (Equation 4.13) so that E is the subject.

Reversing the equation gives:

$$\frac{E}{t} = P$$

Multiplying both sides by t gives:

$$\frac{Et}{t} = Pt$$

The t terms on the left-hand side cancel to give:

$$E = Pt$$

Substituting $P = 2.0$ kW $= 2000$ W and $t = 150$ s, and remembering that 1 W $= 1$ J s^{-1}, gives:

$$E = 2000 \text{ W} \times 150 \text{ s}$$

$$= 2000 \times 150 \text{ J s}^{-1} \times \text{s}$$

$$= 3.0 \times 10^5 \text{ J to two significant figures}$$

Note that, since $s^{-1} = \dfrac{1}{s}$, the units of s^{-1} and s cancel to give final units of J, as expected for energy.

Question 4.6

1 Decide how you are going to tackle the problem

You are trying to find the length of time, t, that the golf ball and the club are in contact.

You have been told:

mass of golf ball, $m = 5.0 \times 10^{-2}$ kg

final speed, $v = 75$ m s^{-1}

mean power, $P = 3.1$ kW $= 3.1 \times 10^3$ W

Possible equations:

$$E_k = \tfrac{1}{2}mv^2 \quad \text{(Equation 3.1)}$$

$$P = \frac{E}{t} \quad \text{(Equation 4.13)}$$

Assumptions

The initial speed of the golf ball is zero so you can assume that the energy transferred, E, to the ball is equal to the ball's final kinetic energy, E_k.

Plan

You can use the known values of m and v to find kinetic energy from $E_k = \tfrac{1}{2}mv^2$.

Then you can rearrange $P = \dfrac{E}{t}$ to make t the subject and substitute the value you have found for kinetic energy (since $E = E_k$) and the known value of P. This should give a value for the time, t.

2 Do the calculation

$$E_k = \frac{1}{2}mv^2$$

$$= \frac{1}{2} \times 5.0 \times 10^{-2} \text{ kg} \times (75 \text{ m s}^{-1})^2$$

$$= 140.625 \text{ kg m}^2 \text{ s}^{-2}$$

$$= 140.625 \text{ J}$$

Multiplying both sides of $P = \dfrac{E}{t}$ by t gives:

$$Pt = E$$

Dividing both sides by P gives:

$$t = \frac{E}{P}$$

The initial speed of the golf ball is zero so the energy transferred, E, to the ball is equal to the ball's final kinetic energy, E_k, so:

$$t = \frac{E_k}{P}$$
$$= \frac{140.625 \text{ J}}{3.1 \times 10^3 \text{ W}}$$
$$= \frac{140.625 \text{ J}}{3.1 \times 10^3 \text{ J s}^{-1}}$$
$$= 4.5 \times 10^{-2} \text{ s}$$

All of the initial values were given to two significant figures so the answer is also given to two significant figures.

In working out the units, note that the joules on the right-hand side cancel and that $\frac{1}{s^{-1}} = s$.

3 Check that your answer makes sense

Repeating the calculation with approximated values of $v \approx 80 \text{ m s}^{-1}$ and $P \approx 4 \times 10^3$ W gives:

$$E_k = \frac{1}{2}mv^2$$
$$\approx \frac{1}{2} \times 5 \times 10^{-2} \text{ kg} \times (80 \text{ m s}^{-1})^2$$
$$\approx 160 \text{ J}$$

$$t = \frac{E_k}{P}$$
$$\approx \frac{160 \text{ J}}{4 \times 10^3 \text{ W}}$$
$$\approx 4 \times 10^{-2} \text{ s}$$

So the calculated value is of approximately the correct size.

The units have worked out to be seconds, as expected for units of time.

Question 5.1

(a) A person with mass m has weight mg. On the Earth $g = 9.8 \text{ m s}^{-2}$, so the weight of a 76 kg person is:

$$\text{weight} = 76 \text{ kg} \times 9.8 \text{ m s}^{-2}$$
$$= 744.8 \text{ kg m s}^{-2}$$
$$= 7.4 \times 10^2 \text{ N to two significant figures}$$

(remembering that 1 kg m s^{-2} = 1 N)

(b) On the Moon $g = 1.6$ m s^{-2} so, in this case:

$$\text{weight} = 76 \text{ kg} \times 1.6 \text{ m s}^{-2}$$
$$= 121.6 \text{ kg m s}^{-2}$$
$$= 1.2 \times 10^2 \text{ N to two significant figures}$$

Question 5.2

(a) The work done by gravity is $W = mgh$. You are asked to estimate the work done, so you need to estimate values for the mass of the book and for the height of your table. Possible estimates are $m = 1$ kg and $h = 0.8$ m. With these values, and using a value for g of 10 m s^{-2}, the work done on the book by gravity as it falls is:

$$W = mgh$$
$$= 1 \text{ kg} \times 10 \text{ m s}^{-2} \times 0.8 \text{ m}$$
$$= 8 \text{ kg m}^2 \text{ s}^{-2}$$
$$= 8 \text{ J to one significant figure}$$

[Your estimated values may have been somewhat different, but your answer shouldn't differ from this by more than a factor of two. If it does, think again about your estimated values.]

(b) The kinetic energy just before impact will be equal to the work done, so it is 8 J too. You can work out the speed from this kinetic energy using Equation 3.3:

$$v = \sqrt{\frac{2E_k}{m}}$$

Substituting $E_k = 8$ J and $m = 1$ kg gives

$$v = \sqrt{\frac{2 \times 8 \text{ J}}{1 \text{ kg}}}$$
$$= \sqrt{\frac{2 \times 8 \text{ kg m}^2 \text{ s}^{-2}}{1 \text{ kg}}}$$
$$= \sqrt{16 \text{ m}^2 \text{ s}^{-2}}$$
$$= 4 \text{ m s}^{-1} \text{ to one significant figure}$$

(c) The kinetic energy will be zero after the book comes to rest on the floor. However, energy is always conserved, so the kinetic energy must be converted into other forms of energy, in particular, to sound energy and internal energy of the book and the floor.

Question 5.3

(a) The change in gravitational potential energy is calculated from $\Delta E_g = mg\Delta h$ (Equation 5.8), so substituting the values of mass ($m = 80$ kg) and height difference ($\Delta h = 5.5$ cm $= 0.055$ m) quoted in the question, gives:

$$\Delta E_g = 80 \text{ kg} \times 9.8 \text{ m s}^{-2} \times 0.055 \text{ m}$$
$$= 43.12 \text{ kg m}^2 \text{ s}^{-2}$$
$$= 43 \text{ J to two significant figures}$$

(b) The speed of the bob is zero at the highest point of the swing, so its kinetic energy is zero there too. As the bob swings down, gravitational potential energy is converted into kinetic energy, and the kinetic energy will be greatest at the lowest point, where the gravitational potential energy has its lowest value. Therefore, this is the point where the speed is at its maximum value.

Assuming that air resistance is negligible, conservation of energy tells you that the maximum kinetic energy of the pendulum is equal to the decrease in its gravitational potential energy so:

$$E_k = \tfrac{1}{2}mv^2 = \Delta E_g$$

Multiplying both sides of $\tfrac{1}{2}mv^2 = \Delta E_g$ by 2 and dividing by m, gives:

$$v^2 = \frac{2\Delta E_g}{m}$$

so:

$$v = \sqrt{\frac{2\Delta E_g}{m}}$$
$$= \sqrt{\frac{2 \times 43.12 \text{ J}}{80 \text{ kg}}}$$
$$= \sqrt{\frac{2 \times 43.12 \text{ kg m}^2 \text{ s}^{-2}}{80 \text{ kg}}}$$
$$= \sqrt{1.078 \text{ m}^2 \text{ s}^{-2}}$$
$$= 1.0 \text{ m s}^{-1} \text{ to two significant figures}$$

[Note that the information about the length of the cable and the distance through which the bob swings was not needed to answer this question, but was included for interest, and to give you practice in selecting the information needed to answer questions. Note also that the value for ΔE_g used in the second half of the question (43.12 J) is given to more than the two significant figures required in the final answer. This is to avoid the danger of rounding errors (see Activity 4.2).]

Question 5.4

1 Decide how you are going to tackle the problem

The information in the question can be summarised in a diagram such as Figure 5.12.

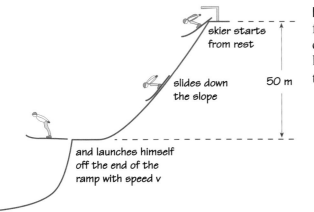

skier starts
from rest

slides down
the slope

50 m

and launches himself
off the end of the
ramp with speed v

Figure 5.12 A skier starts from rest, slides down a ramp of vertical height 50 m and launches himself off the end of the ramp with speed v.

You need to find the speed of the skier v as he launches himself off the end of the ramp. The skier starts from rest at the top of the ramp.

$\Delta h = 50$ m and you can assume $g = 9.8$ m s^{-2}.

You don't know the skier's mass.

The equations to use are:

$E_k = \frac{1}{2}mv^2$ (Equation 3.1)

$\Delta E_g = mg\Delta h$ (Equation 5.8)

Assumption

There is no friction or air resistance.

Plan

If you assume no friction or air resistance, all the gravitational potential energy at the top of the ramp is converted into kinetic energy at the bottom, i.e. $\Delta E_g = E_k$. So you can equate Equations 5.8 and 3.1.

You can divide both sides of the resultant equation by m, so it won't matter that you don't know the skier's mass.

You can then rearrange the equation to make v the subject and substitute values for g and Δh to find v.

2 Do the calculation

Equating Equation 3.1 and Equation 5.8:

$\frac{1}{2}mv^2 = mg\Delta h$

Dividing both sides by m:

$\frac{1}{2}v^2 = g\Delta h$

Multiplying both sides by 2:

$$v^2 = 2g\Delta h$$

Taking the square root of both sides:

$$v = \sqrt{2g\Delta h}$$

Substituting values for Δh and g:

$$v = \sqrt{2 \times 9.8 \text{ m s}^{-2} \times 50 \text{ m}} = \sqrt{980 \text{ m}^2 \text{ s}^{-2}} = 31 \text{ m s}^{-1}$$

Assuming that the vertical height is known to the nearest metre, 50 m is known to two significant figures. So the answer is also given to two significant figures.

In working out the units on the right-hand side, you take the square root of $\text{m}^2 \text{ s}^{-2}$ to give m s^{-1}.

3   Check that your answer makes sense

The units work out to be m s^{-1}, as expected for units of speed.

Repeating the calculation with an approximate value of g of 9 m s^{-2} (chosen because it gives a value for $2g\Delta h$ that it is relatively easy to find the square root of) gives:

$$v \approx \sqrt{2 \times 9 \text{ m s}^{-2} \times 50 \text{ m}} \approx \sqrt{900 \text{ m}^2 \text{ s}^{-2}} \approx 30 \text{ m s}^{-1}$$

so the calculated value is approximately the correct size.

[In reality, neither of the assumptions made in this question is valid. Much of the skill of the ski-jumper lies in correctly waxing the skis to reduce the friction and in adopting a good aerodynamic position to reduce air resistance. Even so, the effects of friction and air resistance cannot be eliminated altogether. These effects act to reduce the skier's launch speed. However, experienced ski-jumpers 'spring' off the end of the ramp, which helps to increase their speed and kinetic energy.]

Question 6.1

(a) You can calculate the energy required to heat the copper pan using Equation 6.5, $q = mc\Delta T$, and substituting the values $c = 3.8 \times 10^2 \text{ J kg}^{-1}\,^\circ\text{C}^{-1}$ (from Table 6.1), $m = 0.50 \text{ kg}$, and $\Delta T = 80\,^\circ\text{C}$:

$$q = 0.50 \text{ kg} \times 3.8 \times 10^2 \text{ J kg}^{-1}\,^\circ\text{C}^{-1} \times 80\,^\circ\text{C} = 1.5 \times 10^4 \text{ J}$$

(b) (i) A 250 g (0.25 kg) copper pan has half the mass of the 0.50 kg pan in (a). Since the energy required is proportional to the mass, this smaller pan requires half of the energy that you calculated as the answer to (a), i.e. $\frac{1}{2} \times 1.5 \times 10^4 \text{ J} = 7.5 \times 10^3 \text{ J}$.

(ii) The energy required is also proportional to the specific heat capacity of the material from which the pan is made. The specific heat capacity of aluminium is greater than that of copper, so the energy required to heat it is greater. Since you were asked to 'estimate', you can say that the specific heat capacity of aluminium (Table 6.1) is about twice that of copper, so the energy required is about double the value calculated in (a), i.e. $2 \times 1.5 \times 10^4 \text{ J} = 3 \times 10^4 \text{ J}$.

[This estimate is made for copper and aluminium pans that have the same mass. In practice, because aluminium has a much lower density than copper, the energy required for pans with similar dimensions is approximately the same. However, copper pans conduct heat better than aluminium, so many cooks prefer them for this reason.]

Question 6.2

(a) To find the temperature in kelvin, you add 273.15 to the numerical value of the temperature in degrees Celsius. So the boiling temperature of liquid oxygen is $(-183 + 273.15) \text{ K} = 90 \text{ K}$.

[Note that the answer is given to the nearest kelvin, because the Celsius temperature was given to the nearest °C.]

(b) Assuming that all of the heat q transferred to the flask provides the latent heat to vaporise liquid oxygen, $q = L_v m$, where L_v is the value of the specific latent heat of vaporisation for oxygen (given in Table 6.2 as $2.1 \times 10^5 \text{ J kg}^{-1}$) and m is the mass that is vaporised. Rearranging this equation to make m the subject:

$$m = \frac{q}{L_v} = \frac{9.5 \times 10^4 \text{ J}}{2.1 \times 10^5 \text{ J kg}^{-1}} = 0.45 \text{ kg}$$

In working out the units on the right-hand side, the joules cancel and the fact that $\frac{1}{\text{kg}^{-1}} = \text{kg}$ is used.

Since the value of the heat transferred used in the calculation is the amount transferred in an hour, the mass of 0.45 kg is the mass vaporised in an hour.

Question 6.3

(a) You have $m = 1.0 \text{ kg}$ and $L_f = 3.3 \times 10^5 \text{ J kg}^{-1}$.

From Equation 6.9:

$$q = L_f m = 3.3 \times 10^5 \text{ J kg}^{-1} \times 1.0 \text{ kg} = 3.3 \times 10^5 \text{ J}$$

(b) You have $m = 1.0 \text{ kg}$, $c = 4.2 \times 10^3 \text{ J kg}^{-1} \text{ °C}^{-1}$ and $\Delta T = 100 \text{ °C}$.

From Equation 6.5:

$$q = mc\Delta T = 1.0 \text{ kg} \times 4.2 \times 10^3 \text{ J kg}^{-1} \text{ °C}^{-1} \times 100 \text{ °C} = 4.2 \times 10^5 \text{ J}$$

(c) You have $m = 1.0 \text{ kg}$ and $L_v = 2.3 \times 10^6 \text{ J kg}^{-1}$.

From Equation 6.8:

$$q = L_v m = 2.3 \times 10^6 \text{ J kg}^{-1} \times 1.0 \text{ kg} = 2.3 \times 10^6 \text{ J}$$

[Note that the answer to (c) is larger than the answers to (a) and (b). More energy is required to evaporate one kilogram of water than is required to heat the same mass from 0 °C to 100 °C, or to melt one kilogram of ice.]

Question 7.1

If you assume a person of mass 65 kg, there are about 65×10^{26} electrons in their body, or 6.5×10^{27} using scientific notation. The total charge of all of the electrons is the number of electrons multiplied by the charge on each electron, so the charge of electrons is $(6.5 \times 10^{27}) \times (-1.602 \times 10^{-19}$ C$)$.

This is about -1×10^9 C. Since the person is electrically neutral, there must also be a total positive charge of $+1 \times 10^9$ C in their body.

[You will have a different mass and, therefore, the charges that you have estimated will be different; however, they are unlikely to differ from the answers above by more than a factor of about two.]

Question 7.2

Atoms are electrically neutral overall because each atom has equal amounts of negative and positive charge. So, as you are made of atoms, your body as a whole is electrically neutral. As there is no electrical force between neutral objects, there can be no electrical force between you and another person in the same room.

Alternatively, you may argue that two humans will have repulsive forces (i) between their 10^9 C of negative charge and (ii) between their 10^9 C of positive charge. However, then you would have to argue that there is also the same size attractive forces (i) between the 10^9 C of negative charge of one of the humans and the 10^9 C of positive charge of the other and (ii) between the 10^9 C of positive charge of the first and the 10^9 C of negative charge of the second. The total repulsive force will exactly cancel out the total attractive force, so the two humans can safely sit together.

Question 7.3

Reversing Equation 7.1, $I = \dfrac{Q}{t}$, gives:

$$\frac{Q}{t} = I$$

Multiplying both sides by t gives:

$$Q = It$$

In this case, $I = 5$ A $= 5$ C s^{-1} and $t = 10$ minutes $= 10 \times 60$ s $= 600$ s, so:

$$Q = It = 5\,\text{C s}^{-1} \times 600\,\text{s} = 3 \times 10^3\,\text{C}$$

Note that the SI units of electric current are amperes and 1 A $= 1$ C s^{-1}. Thus the SI units of the answer work out to be C s$^{-1} \times$ s $=$ C.

Question 7.4

From Equation 7.9:

$$R = \frac{\Delta V}{I} = \frac{1.5\,\text{V}}{0.3\,\text{A}} = 5\,\Omega$$

Question 7.5

Since $\Delta V = RI$ (Equation 7.8), the resistance R can be found by calculating the gradient of a graph of ΔV against I (this is what is plotted in Figure 7.14):

$$\text{gradient} = \frac{\text{rise}}{\text{run}}$$

$$= \frac{(2.35 - 0)\ \text{V}}{(5.0 - 0) \times 10^{-3}\ \text{A}}$$

$$= \frac{2.35\ \text{V}}{5.0 \times 10^{-3}\ \text{A}}$$

$$= 470\ \Omega \text{ to two significant figures}$$

So the resistance is 470 Ω.

Question 7.6

(a) First, you need to rearrange Equation 7.15, $P = I\Delta V$, to make I the subject. Reversing the equation and dividing both sides by ΔV gives:

$$I = \frac{P}{\Delta V}$$

Substituting the values for the power (20 W) and the voltage difference (12 V) into this equation gives:

$$I = \frac{20\ \text{W}}{12\ \text{V}} = 1.67\ \text{A} \quad \text{or } 1.7\ \text{A to two significant figures}$$

(b) First, rearrange Equation 7.1, $I = \frac{Q}{t}$, to make Q the subject. Reversing the equation and multiplying both sides by t gives $Q = It$.

Substituting for I (1.67 A) and t (60 s) gives:

$$Q = 1.67\ \text{A} \times 60\ \text{s}$$

$$= 100.2\ \text{A s}$$

$$= 100.2\ \text{C s}^{-1} \times \text{s}$$

$$= 1.0 \times 10^2\ \text{C to two significant figures}$$

Question 8.1

The absorption spectrum in Figure 8.10 contains absorption lines at precisely the same locations (that is, the same colours) as the emission lines in the hydrogen spectrum in Figure 8.9. Since the two spectra have the same 'spectral fingerprint', the unknown vapour must be hydrogen.

[Note that the spectral fingerprint can be either an emission or an absorption spectrum and this question shows how the two are related.]

Question 8.2

Since $1\,\text{eV} = 1.6 \times 10^{-19}\,\text{J}$, $1\,\text{J} = \dfrac{1\,\text{eV}}{1.6 \times 10^{-19}}$.

So the energy of a photon of green light is:

$$3.8 \times 10^{-19}\,\text{J} = 3.8 \times 10^{-19} \times \frac{1\,\text{eV}}{1.6 \times 10^{-19}} = 2.4\,\text{eV}$$

[In general, to convert from joules to electronvolts you need to multiply by $\dfrac{1\,\text{eV}}{1.6 \times 10^{-19}\,\text{J}}$. Conversely, to convert from electronvolts to joules, multiply by $\dfrac{1.6 \times 10^{-19}\,\text{J}}{1\,\text{eV}}$.]

Question 8.3

(a) Figure 8.7b shows that the spectrum of light from a sodium lamp is an emission spectrum. You know from the accompanying text that the strongest emission is for yellow light, with a photon energy, E_{ph}, of about 2.1 eV. So the spectral distribution has a large 'spike' at this energy (Figure 8.18a).

(b) The continuous spectrum of light from the tungsten filament lamp is absorbed by the sodium vapour atoms. However, absorption only occurs at specific energies (Figure 8.7c). The resulting spectral distribution is that of an absorption spectrum, with strong absorption at an energy, E_{ph}, of 2.1 eV (Figure 8.18b).

Figure 8.18   Sketches for the answer to Question 8.3.

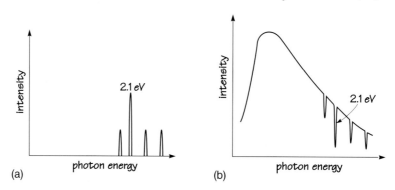

Question 8.4

(a) From Figure 8.16, you can see that the energy of each photon of microwave is about 10^{-25} to 10^{-21} J.

(b) From Figure 8.16, you can see that the energy of each X-ray photon is around 10^2 to 10^6 eV or about 0.1 keV to 1 MeV. [Dental X-rays are typically less than 100 keV.]

Question 9.1

(a) If five peaks travel past a fixed point in two seconds, the time interval between one peak and the next is $\dfrac{2\,\text{s}}{5} = 0.4\,\text{s}$. The period of the wave is therefore 0.4 seconds.

(b) You can think of the frequency of the wave as simply the number of peaks that pass a fixed point in one second. In this case, five peaks pass a fixed point in two seconds, so 2.5 peaks pass by in one second, i.e. the frequency is 2.5 Hz.

Alternatively, you can see that, since $f = \dfrac{1}{T}$, $f = \dfrac{1}{0.4 \text{ s}} = 2.5 \text{ s}^{-1}$ or 2.5 Hz.

Question 9.2

(a) The period of a wave is the time interval between successive instants when similar parts of the wave profile pass a particular point. Since Figure 9.5b shows the behaviour of a wave over *time* at a particular point in *space*, the period of the wave can be measured as the time between successive peaks, or successive troughs, of the wave, for instance. In Figure 9.5b, the peaks of the wave occur at times $t = 0.5$ s, $t = 2.5$ s and $t = 4.5$ s. Hence the period of the wave is $T = 2.0$ s.

(b) The frequency of the wave is defined as $f = \dfrac{1}{T}$, so $f = \dfrac{1}{2.0 \text{ s}} = 0.50 \text{ Hz}$.

(c) The amplitude A of a wave is defined as the maximum displacement of the wave above and below its mean value, or half the peak-to-trough height. From Figure 9.5b, the amplitude of the wave is 3.0 cm.

(d) It is impossible to determine the speed of propagation of this wave using only Figure 9.5b.

[In order to calculate the speed, you need to know the wavelength as well as the frequency. Figure 9.5a contains such information. If these two figures illustrate the *same* wave, the *combined* information from the two graphs is sufficient to specify the wave completely. Figure 9.5b yields the period, $T = 2.0$ s (and frequency, $f = 0.50$ Hz) and Figure 9.5a yields the wavelength, $\lambda = 10.0$ cm. These two values then enable the wave speed to be calculated, using Equation 9.1, $v = f\lambda = 0.50 \text{ Hz} \times 10.0 \text{ cm} = 5.0 \text{ cm s}^{-1}$ which is equivalent to $5.0 \times 10^{-2} \text{ m s}^{-1}$.]

Question 9.3

All light, whether red, green or any other colour, travels at the same speed in a vacuum, $c = 3.00 \times 10^8 \text{ m s}^{-1}$. Since Equation 9.2 indicates that the wavelength and frequency of a light wave are related by $c = f\lambda$, multiplying the frequency and wavelength for red light must give the same value as multiplying the frequency and wavelength for green light. Therefore, if red light has a longer (i.e. greater) wavelength than green light, red light must have a smaller frequency than green light.

Question 9.4

(a) $\sin 10° = 0.174$

(b) $\sin 60° = 0.866$

(c) $\sin 30° = 0.500$

(d) $\sin 0° = 0.000$

[In fact, the sine of 30° is exactly $\frac{1}{2}$ and the sine of 0° is exactly 0.]

Question 9.5

Start by rearranging Equation 9.4 to make d the subject.

Multiplying both sides by d gives $d \sin \theta_n = n\lambda$.

Dividing both sides by $\sin \theta_n$ gives:

$$d = \frac{n\lambda}{\sin \theta_n}$$

We know $\lambda = 572$ nm, and since 1 nm $= 1 \times 10^{-9}$ m, then

$$\lambda = 572 \times 10^{-9} \text{ m} = 5.72 \times 10^{-7} \text{ m}$$

When $n = 4$, $\theta_n = 43.7°$, so $\sin \theta_n = 0.6909$ to four significant figures.

Thus:

$$d = \frac{4 \times 5.72 \times 10^{-7} \text{ m}}{0.6909} = 3.31 \times 10^{-6} \text{ m to three significant figures}$$

So the diffraction grating has a spacing of 3.31 μm.

Question 9.6

(a) 1 kHz corresponds to 10^3 Hz, 1 MHz corresponds to 10^6 Hz, and 1 GHz corresponds to 10^9 Hz. The first two are within the radio wave part of the spectrum. The third is on the boundary between radio waves and microwaves.

(b) Since 1 nm corresponds to 10^{-9} m, it should be marked on the wavelength axis somewhere between 3×10^{-10} m and 3×10^{-9} m. This is near the boundary between the ultraviolet and X-ray parts of the spectrum.

Since 1 μm corresponds to 10^{-6} m, it should be marked on the wavelength axis somewhere between 3×10^{-7} m and 3×10^{-6} m. This is in the infrared part of the spectrum, at a slightly longer wavelength than red light. [From the insert to Figure 9.10 you can see that the longest wavelength of visible radiation is about 7×10^{-7} m.]

Since 1 mm corresponds to 10^{-3} m, it should be written on the wavelength axis somewhere between 3×10^{-4} m and 3×10^{-3} m. This is in the microwave part of the spectrum.

[Note that marking points on a powers of ten scale is tricky, so you can mark these positions only very approximately.]

Question 9.7

(a) Equation 9.2 can be rearranged to give $\lambda = \dfrac{c}{f}$ where $c = 3.00 \times 10^8$ m s^{-1} and $f = 2.45$ GHz $= 2.45 \times 10^9$ Hz. So

$$\lambda = \frac{3.00 \times 10^8 \text{ m s}^{-1}}{2.45 \times 10^9 \text{ s}^{-1}} = 0.122 \text{ m}$$

The microwaves have a wavelength of 0.122 m, i.e. 12.2 cm.

(b) Equation 9.2 can be rearranged to give $f = \dfrac{c}{\lambda}$ where $c = 3.00 \times 10^8$ m s^{-1} and $\lambda = 8.8 \times 10^{-12}$ m. So

$$f = \frac{3.00 \times 10^8 \text{ m s}^{-1}}{8.8 \times 10^{-12} \text{ m}} = 3.4 \times 10^{19} \text{ s}^{-1} = 3.4 \times 10^{19} \text{ Hz}$$

[Note that, according to Figure 9.10, this is in the X-ray region of the electromagnetic spectrum, not the gamma-ray region. This indicates the overlapping nature of the different regions. Although gamma rays are generally higher frequency than X-rays, they are usually distinguished by their different method of production rather than their different frequency or wavelength.]

Question 10.1

$E_{ph} = 511$ keV $= 511 \times 10^3$ eV $= 5.11 \times 10^5$ eV

Equation 10.2 can be rearranged to make λ the subject:

$$\lambda = \frac{hc}{E_{ph}}$$
$$= \frac{(4.14 \times 10^{-15} \text{ eV Hz}^{-1}) \times (3.00 \times 10^8 \text{ m s}^{-1})}{5.11 \times 10^5 \text{ eV}}$$
$$= 2.43 \times 10^{-12} \text{ m}$$

The wavelength of the radiation corresponding to the X-ray photon is therefore 2.43×10^{-12} m.

Question 10.2

First, convert the frequency of the radiation into the equivalent energy of each photon in electronvolts. Using Equation 10.1:

$$E_{ph} = hf$$
$$= (4.14 \times 10^{-15} \text{ eV Hz}^{-1}) \times (1.5 \times 10^{15} \text{ Hz})$$
$$= 6.2 \text{ eV}$$

Now it is simply a matter of applying the law of conservation of energy as expressed by Equation 10.5, namely $E_{k, \max} = E_{ph} - E_0 = (6.2 - 4.6)$ eV $= 1.6$ eV. So the maximum kinetic energy of the photoelectrons is 1.6 eV.

Question 10.3

(a) Equation 10.2 gives the photon energy corresponding to a wavelength of 152 nm as:

$$E_{ph} = \frac{hc}{\lambda}$$
$$= \frac{(4.14 \times 10^{-15} \text{ eV Hz}^{-1}) \times (3.00 \times 10^8 \text{ m s}^{-1})}{152 \times 10^{-9} \text{ m}}$$
$$= 8.17 \text{ eV}$$

(b) Photons with an energy of 8.17 eV cause electrons to be emitted with a maximum kinetic energy of 6.30 eV. Equation 10.5, $E_{k, max} = E_{ph} - E_0$, can be rearranged to make E_0 the subject (by adding E_0 to both sides and then subtracting $E_{k, max}$ from both sides):

$$E_0 = E_{ph} - E_{k, max} = (8.17 - 6.30) \text{ eV} = 1.87 \text{ eV}$$

Thus the minimum energy needed to eject electrons from the metal is 1.87 eV.

The wavelength of radiation corresponding to photons that have this energy is obtained by applying Equation 10.2 again. This time:

$$\lambda = \frac{hc}{E_0}$$

$$= \frac{(4.14 \times 10^{-15} \text{ eV Hz}^{-1}) \times (3.00 \times 10^8 \text{ m s}^{-1})}{1.87 \text{ eV}}$$

$$= 6.64 \times 10^{-7} \text{ m}$$

The wavelength of radiation corresponding to the lowest energy photons that can free electrons from the metal is therefore about 664 nm, in the visible (red) part of the spectrum.

(c) Since infrared radiation has a longer wavelength than visible radiation (light), the energy of photons of infrared radiation is less than 1.87 eV. Therefore, these photons have insufficient energy to free electrons from the metal.

Question 11.1

(a) Clearly, the spectra of both the tungsten filament light bulb and the energy-saving light bulb differ greatly from the spectra of the lasers that you saw in Activity 9.1. A laser produces light of a single colour – it is like having a single spectral line. So the diffraction pattern of laser light contains just a single point or line in each order of the diffraction pattern. On the other hand, the two light bulbs each produce white light – a mixture of colours – and the diffraction grating allows you to see what that mix of colours is. In addition, the spectra for the lasers take the form of dots whereas, for the light bulbs, the images are of the same height as the slit in the cardboard.

(b) The tungsten filament bulb produces a continuous spectrum – the spectrum contains light of *all* colours, so all wavelengths or frequencies in the visible region of the electromagnetic spectrum are present. On the other hand, the energy-saving bulb produces a line spectrum – the spectrum contains light of only discrete colours, and these appear as bright lines in the spectrum. The discrete colours correspond to specific wavelengths and frequencies within the visible part of the electromagnetic spectrum. The spectra from both types of light bulb are emission spectra.

Question 11.2

In Section 8.5, the continuous spectral distribution of a tungsten filament was discussed, and the peak of its intensity was shown to be in the infrared part of the spectrum. All the radiation that is emitted outside the visible part of the spectrum is 'wasted', since it doesn't help to illuminate things for human eyes to see. Typically, 60 J of electrical energy per second (60 W) is supplied to such a bulb, but only a small fraction of this energy appears as light. All the infrared radiation merely heats up the surroundings of the bulb, as you will have noted.

By contrast, an energy-saving light bulb emits its radiation in a series of spectral lines, most of which are in the visible part of the spectrum. Relatively little energy is 'wasted' by providing emission elsewhere in the spectrum. As a result, such a bulb needs much less electrical energy (typically only 12 J of electrical energy per second) to get the same intensity in the visible part of the spectrum as with a 60 W tungsten filament bulb. Also, there is very little infrared radiation from energy-saving bulbs, so they don't get so hot.

Comments on activities

Activity 3.1

(a) In this case, the symbol F represents the magnitude of the unbalanced force on an object; m represents the object's mass, and a represents the magnitude of the object's acceleration. Remembering that there is a 'hidden' multiplication sign in $F = ma$ (i.e. the equation could be written as $F = m \times a$), in words $F = ma$ means 'the magnitude of the unbalanced force on an object is equal to the mass of that object multiplied by the magnitude of its acceleration'. This is Newton's second law of motion.

(b) m (mass) is measured in kg (kilograms), a (acceleration) is measured in m s^{-2} (metres per second squared) and F (force) is measured in N (newtons). Note that it is important to use a capital N as the symbol for the newton (even though the name of the unit is written with a lower-case n) and to use lower case k, g, m and s when writing kg and m s^{-2}. Remember also that the spaces between units are important, so you should write m s^{-2} *not* ms^{-2}. The equation $F = ma$ is a reminder that $1 \text{ N} = 1 \text{ kg} \times 1 \text{ m s}^{-2}$, or $1 \text{ N} = 1 \text{ kg m s}^{-2}$. The importance of units is discussed in more detail later in this book, especially in the *Working out the Units* video sequence in Activity 4.2.

(c) The word equation is:

$$\text{power} = \frac{\text{energy transferred}}{\text{time taken}}$$

If you chose the letters P to represent power, E to represent energy transferred and T to represent time taken, your equation would be:

$$P = \frac{E}{T}$$

Choosing the letters P, E and T to represent power, energy and time is quite reasonable, and P and E are indeed the symbols conventionally used to represent power and energy. However, it is conventional to use a lower-case t to represent time, reserving capital T for temperature. So the equation is more conventionally written as:

$$P = \frac{E}{t}$$

(d) $E = 3.4 \times 10^5$ J and $t = 2$ minutes 15 seconds $= (2 \times 60)$ s $+ 15$ s $= 135$ s.

Substituting these values into the equation gives:

$$P = \frac{E}{t}$$
$$= \frac{3.4 \times 10^5 \text{ J}}{135 \text{ s}}$$
$$= 2.5185 \times 10^3 \frac{\text{J}}{\text{s}}$$
$$= 2.5 \times 10^3 \text{ J s}^{-1} \text{ to two significant figures}$$

Since a joule per second is equal to a watt (symbol W) (from Book 1, Section 4.1) the power could alternatively be written as 2.5×10^3 W.

Notes

The units are as important a part of the answer as the numerical value. In this case, the units of time were converted into SI units (seconds) before the calculation was done. The units of joules (J) were then divided by seconds (s) to give units of $\dfrac{J}{s}$ in the answer, which could be written as J s^{-1} or W.

The energy was given to two significant figures and, when in seconds, the time was quoted to three significant figures, so the final answer is given to *two* significant figures (see Book 1, Section 3.1.4).

If you found the maths in this activity difficult, you may want to consider setting aside more time for studying the rest of Book 3, since there is quite a lot of maths in it. If you have serious anxieties, you are advised to contact your tutor.

Several new symbols and equations are introduced in this book and Activity 4.1 will encourage you to produce your own glossary of them. This will help you to become familiar with their use.

Activity 4.2

I   Decide how you are going to tackle the problem

The information in the question can be summarised in a sketch such as Figure 4.6.

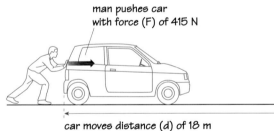

man pushes car
with force (F) of 415 N

car moves distance (d) of 18 m
in a time (t) of 36 s

What is the power (P)?

Figure 4.6   A broken-down car being pushed.

You are trying to find the mean power, *P*:

force $F = 415$ N

distance $d = 18$ m

time $t = 36$ s

The equations you might use are:

$$P = \frac{E}{t} \text{ (Equation 4.13)}$$

$$W = Fd \text{ (Equation 4.8)}$$

$$F = ma \text{ (Book 2, Equation 14.2)}$$

[Note that you only need to use the first two of these equations, but it is better to write down too many possible equations than too few.]

Assumptions

- the applied force is in the direction of motion of the car
- the energy converted (E) is equal to the work (W) that the man does in pushing the car.

Plan

There are at least two different methods of solving this problem. Just one method is given here, but Chapter 5 discusses an alternative method, which leaves the quantities as symbols for longer before substituting values into the equations.

You can substitute the values given for F and d into $W = Fd$ to find the work done W. Then, since $E = W$, you can substitute this value for E and the value given for t into $P = \dfrac{E}{t}$ to find the mean power, P.

2   Do the calculation

$$W = Fd$$
$$= 415\ \text{N} \times 18\ \text{m}$$
$$= 7470\ \text{N m}$$
$$= 7470\ \text{J} \quad \text{since} \quad 1\ \text{J} = 1\ \text{N m}$$

$E = W$ so:

$$P = \frac{E}{t}$$
$$= \frac{7470\ \text{J}}{36\ \text{s}}$$
$$= 207.5\ \text{J s}^{-1}$$
$$= 2.1 \times 10^2\ \text{W to two significant figures}$$

[The value for F was given to three significant figures but the values for d and t were given to two significant figures, so the answer should be given to two significant figures.]

3   Check that your answer makes sense

Repeating the calculation with approximate values of $F \approx 400$ N, $d \approx 20$ m and $t \approx 40$ s gives:

$$W = Fd$$
$$\approx 400\ \text{N} \times 20\ \text{m}$$
$$\approx 8000\ \text{J}$$

$$P = \frac{E}{t}$$
$$\approx \frac{8000\ \text{J}}{40\ \text{s}}$$
$$\approx 200\ \text{W}$$

So, the calculated value is approximately the correct size.

The units work out to be watts, as expected for the units of power.

Activity 5.1

1 Decide how you are going to tackle the problem

The information in the question can be summarised in a diagram such as Figure 5.13.

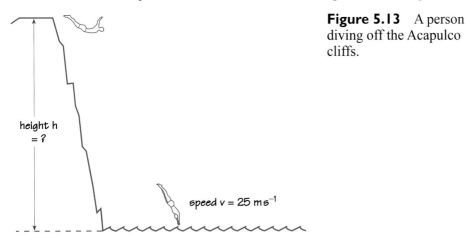

Figure 5.13 A person diving off the Acapulco cliffs.

height h = ?

speed v = 25 m s⁻¹

You are trying to find the height of the cliff, h, and you know that the diver's speed at entry to the water, $v = 25$ m s^{-1}. Note that you don't know the diver's mass.

The equations to use are:

$$E_k = \tfrac{1}{2}mv^2 \quad \text{(Equation 3.1)}$$

$$\Delta E_g = mg\Delta h \quad \text{(Equation 5.8)}$$

Assumptions

- the acceleration due to gravity, g, is 9.8 m s^{-2}
- the diver leaves the cliff with zero speed
- air resistance is negligible. Then, because energy is conserved, the gravitational potential energy that the diver loses is all converted into kinetic energy.

Plan

Because of the assumption, $\Delta E_g = E_k$, you can equate Equations 5.8 and 3.1.

You can divide both sides of the resulting equation by m, so it won't matter that you don't know the diver's mass.

You can then rearrange the equation to make Δh the subject and substitute values for g and v to find Δh, which is the height labelled h in Figure 5.13.

2   Do the calculation

Equating Equations 5.8 and 3.1 gives:

$$mg\,\Delta h = \tfrac{1}{2}mv^2$$

Dividing both sides by m gives:

$$g\,\Delta h = \tfrac{1}{2}v^2$$

Dividing both sides by g gives:

$$\Delta h = \frac{v^2}{2g}$$

Substituting values for v and g:

$$\Delta h = \frac{(25\text{ m s}^{-1})^2}{2 \times 9.8\text{ m s}^{-2}}$$

$$= \frac{625\text{ m}^2\text{ s}^{-2}}{2 \times 9.8\text{ m s}^{-2}}$$

$$= 32\text{ m}$$

All of the values were given to two significant figures so the answer is also given to two significant figures.

[In working out the units on the right-hand side, the s^{-2} in the numerator of the fraction cancelled with the s^{-2} in the denominator. There were units of m^2 (i.e. $\text{m} \times \text{m}$) in the numerator. One m is cancelled with the m in the denominator to leave the final units of the answer as m.]

3   Check that your answer makes sense

The answer is reasonable for the height of a (tall) cliff.

Repeating the calculation with approximate values of $v = 20$ m s^{-1} and $g = 10$ m s^{-2} gives:

$$\Delta h \approx \frac{(20\text{ m s}^{-1})^2}{2 \times 10\text{ m s}^{-2}}$$

$$\approx 20\text{ m}$$

So the calculated value is of approximately the correct size.

The units work out to be metres, as expected for units of height.

This is likely to be an underestimate of the cliff height because you have assumed there is no air resistance. In fact, the diver will be slowed slightly because of air resistance, so the speed with which he hits the water will be lower than if there were no air resistance. This means that the calculated value of Δh will be too small.

Activity 6.1

Task 1

Measuring the mass of water in the kettle

There are various ways you might have thought of doing this. Perhaps the simplest is to use kitchen scales to weigh the kettle when it is empty, and then to weigh it again when it is full of water. The difference between the two measurements is then the mass of water. (If your scales only measure in pounds and ounces, you will need to convert the measurement into kilograms using the conversion factors 1 pound = 0.454 kilograms and 1 ounce = 0.028 kilograms.)

Alternatively, you could weigh some water in a jug and then pour it into the kettle, again taking account of the mass of the jug.

If you don't have any suitable kitchen scales, you could use a measuring jug to pour a measured volume of water into the kettle. The mass m of the water can be calculated from its density ρ and the volume V, using the equation for density $\rho = \dfrac{m}{V}$, which can be rearranged to make m the subject: $m = \rho V$. The density of water is 1000 kg m^{-3}, or 1.000 kg litre^{-1}, so the mass in kilograms is related to the volume in litres by the equation $m = (1.000 \text{ kg litre}^{-1}) \times V$. This means that the numerical value of the mass in kilograms is the same as the numerical value of the volume in litres.

The first method described above is likely to be the most convenient if you have suitable scales.

Determining the temperature change

You may have difficulty deciding how to determine the temperature change without a thermometer. The final temperature is fairly straightforward; if you heat the water to its boiling temperature, it will be at about 100 °C (unless you live at a very high altitude), so this is a reasonable value to use for the final temperature.

There are various ways in which you can start off with water at a known temperature, for example:

- If you leave a jug, or bottle, of water in your kitchen for a few hours, or better still overnight, it will be at room temperature – whatever that is in your kitchen. Most houses are at a temperature within a few degrees of 20 °C, which would be a reasonable estimate to make for the initial temperature.

- You could leave a jug of water in the refrigerator overnight, in which case its temperature would be within one or two degrees of 4 °C, the optimum temperature for a domestic refrigerator.

- If you leave ice in water for long enough, the ice-water mixture will reach a steady temperature of 0 °C and will remain at this temperature until all of the ice has melted. (You must be sure that you don't have any ice in the kettle at the start of the experiment though.)

Decide which method you will use to get water at a known initial temperature, and plan your preparations so that the water is at this temperature when you are ready to start the experiment.

Tasks 2 and 3

Table 6.5 shows a typical set of measurements and how the specific heat was calculated from them.

Table 6.5 Completed version of Table 6.3.

Measurement	Results	Comments
mass of empty kettle	775 g	scales read to 25 g divisions
mass of kettle + water	2200 g	
mass, m, of water in kettle	1425 g = 1.425 kg	
power rating, P, of kettle	2.0 kW = 2000 W	label on bottom
starting time (power on)	6:36:00	used digital watch with seconds display
finishing time (power off)	6:40:34	
time interval, t, for heating	4 min 34 s = 274 s	
starting temperature	20 °C	water stood overnight at room temp.
finishing temperature	100 °C	
temperature change, ΔT	80 °C	
electrical energy supplied, $E = Pt$	5.48×10^5 J	$E = 2.0 \times 10^3$ W $\times$ 274 s = 5.48×10^5 J
specific heat of water, $c = \dfrac{q}{m\Delta T}$	4.8×10^3 J kg^{-1} °C^{-1}	$c = \dfrac{5.48 \times 10^5 \text{ J}}{1.425 \text{ kg} \times 80 \text{ °C}} = 4.8 \times 10^3$ J kg^{-1} °C^{-1}

Task 4

Here is what a course team member noted down after he had completed the experiment (see also Table 6.5). Your notes may be different because you might have tackled the experiment in a different way.

(a) Scales had 25 g divisions, so mass measurements have uncertainty of ±12.5 g.

Water left in kettle overnight before experiment started. Temperature of house about 20 °C, so assume starting temperature 20 °C ± 2 °C.

Assume final temperature 100 °C (normal boiling temperature of water). Therefore, temperature difference 80 °C ± 2 °C.

Time interval difficult to measure – not sure when the water was 'really' boiling; stopped heating when the boiling got fierce, but not sure whether the water reached 100 °C before then. Uncertainty in time about ±10 s.

(b) Some electrical energy goes into internal energy of kettle – it gets hot – and some heats up surrounding air. So not all of energy supplied heats water – heat transferred to water is less than electrical energy supplied, so the true value of specific heat will be less than that calculated.

(c) Largest uncertainty is energy used to heat kettle itself. Therefore need to find way to measure how much energy is used for this in order to get a better value for the specific heat. Could use a thermometer to measure starting temperature.

Note that many experimenters have measured the specific heat of water, and the accepted value (the value published in tables of scientific data) is 4.1796×10^3 J kg^{-1} °C^{-1} at 25 °C and 4.2160×10^3 J kg^{-1} °C^{-1} at 100 °C. To two significant figures this is 4.2×10^3 J kg^{-1} °C^{-1} over the temperature range of this experiment.

Task 5

A suitable conclusion would be as follows.

The value obtained for the specific heat capacity of water in this experiment was 4.8×10^3 J kg^{-1} °C^{-1}. This is about 15% higher than the accepted value, which is 4.2×10^3 J kg^{-1} °C^{-1}. The main reason for this difference is that no allowance was made for the energy that was used to heat the kettle itself or the energy lost to the surrounding air.

You should enter the accepted value in the blank space in Table 6.1. You could also note *your* result below the table.

Activity 6.2

Task 1

The values that you should have inserted into Table 6.4 are 225 g for the mass of water converted into vapour, which is 0.225 kg, and 4 minutes for the time interval for heating, which is 240 seconds.

The calculations could then be written as follows:

Power supplied by kettle, $P = 2.0$ kW $= 2.0 \times 10^3$ W

Time, $t = 240$ s

So the energy supplied, E, is given by

$$E = Pt = 2.0 \times 10^3 \text{ W} \times 240 \text{ s} = 4.8 \times 10^5 \text{ J}$$

Assuming that all this energy is transferred as heat, q, used in vaporising the water:

$$L_v = \frac{q}{m} = \frac{4.8 \times 10^5 \text{ J}}{0.225 \text{ kg}} = 2.1 \times 10^6 \text{ J kg}^{-1} \text{ to two significant figures}$$

Task 2

The course team member made the following notes about the uncertainties.

Measured values of time interval: uncertainty is small, since it is possible to measure the times at which the power is switched on and switched off to the nearest second or less; maximum uncertainty in time interval is ±2 s.

Measured values of mass converted into vapour: with the scales used in this experiment the uncertainty in a mass measurement is probably about half of a scale division, i.e. about 12.5 g. Since the mass converted into vapour is the difference between two measurements of mass, maximum uncertainty in mass evaporated is ±25 g.

Kettle power rating: the rating is specified as 2.0 kW, so I assume that this means that the rating lies between 1.95 kW and 2.05 kW, since values within this range would be rounded to 2.0 kW to two significant figures. So the uncertainty here is ±0.05 kW.

Energy losses from kettle: these uncertainties are difficult to estimate. The water in the kettle must have cooled a little while it was being weighed, so some of the energy supplied in the 4 minute period was used to bring the water back to the boiling temperature. Also, some of the electrical energy was used to heat up the surrounding air rather than to vaporise water. This means that there is an uncertainty in the amount of heat transferred to vaporise the water. Note also that I don't have to worry about energy required to heat the kettle: the vaporisation of the water takes place at the boiling temperature, so the temperature of the kettle is not changing.

[Accounts of experiments often include a separate 'discussion' section, although this can sometimes be part of the results section. The notes here (and your response to Task 2) would form the basis of a discussion section.]

Task 3

Your conclusion should encapsulate the main outcomes of the experiment in two or three sentences. It should include your calculated value for the specific latent heat of vaporisation (Task 1). Note that the accepted value for the latent heat of vaporisation is 2.3×10^6 J kg^{-1} (to two significant figures). You should insert this value in the blank space in Table 6.2.

The course team member wrote the following conclusion:

The value obtained in this experiment for the latent heat of vaporisation of water was 2.1×10^6 J kg^{-1}. This is very close to the accepted value of 2.3×10^6 J kg^{-1}.

Activity 7.1

1   Decide how you are going to tackle the problem

You are trying to find the time, t, taken to heat 150 g of water from 19 °C to 100 °C and to vaporise 50 g (i.e. one-third of 150 g) of water.

You know:

- mass of water to be heated, $m_1 = 150$ g $= 150 \times 10^{-3}$ kg $= 0.15$ kg
- mass of water to be vaporised, $m_2 = 50$ g $= 50 \times 10^{-3}$ kg $= 5.0 \times 10^{-2}$ kg
- temperature rise, $\Delta T = 100$ °C $- 19$ °C $= 81$ °C
- specific heat capacity of water, $c = 4.2 \times 10^3$ J kg^{-1} °C^{-1}
- specific latent heat of vaporisation, $L_v = 2.3 \times 10^6$ J kg^{-1}
- electric current, $I = 13$ A
- voltage difference, $\Delta V = 12$ V

You could use the equations:

$$P = I\Delta V \text{ (Equation 7.15)}$$
$$P = \frac{\Delta E_e}{t} \text{ (Equation 7.13)}$$
$$q = mc\Delta T \text{ (Equation 6.5)}$$
$$q = L_v m \text{ (Equation 6.8)}$$

Assumptions

All the electrical energy supplied is transferred to internal energy in the water.

Plan

You can find the total increase in internal energy from Equation 6.5 (for heating the water) and Equation 6.8 (for vaporising the water).

Since you can assume that all the electrical energy supplied is transferred to internal energy in the water, you then know ΔE_e in Equation 7.13.

You then know both P and ΔE_e, so you can rearrange Equation 7.13 to give the value of t. When actually *doing* the question, it is sensible to start by rearranging Equation 7.13 and then to substitute for P and ΔE_e.

2   Do the calculation

Rearranging Equation 7.13 to make t the subject:

multiply both sides by t

$$Pt = \Delta E_e$$

divide both sides by P

$$t = \frac{\Delta E_e}{P}$$

From Equations 6.5 and 6.8:

$$\Delta E_e = (m_1 c \Delta T) + (L_v m_2)$$

From Equation 7.15:

$$P = I \Delta V$$

so

$$t = \frac{(m_1 c \Delta T) + (L_v m_2)}{I \Delta V}$$

Substituting values:

$$t = \frac{(0.15\ \text{kg} \times 4.2 \times 10^3\ \text{J kg}^{-1}\,{}^{\circ}\text{C}^{-1} \times 81\,{}^{\circ}\text{C}) + (2.3 \times 10^6\ \text{J kg}^{-1} \times 5.0 \times 10^{-2}\ \text{kg})}{13\ \text{A} \times 12\ \text{V}}$$

$$= \frac{(51\,030\ \text{J}) + (115\,000\ \text{J})}{156\ \text{W}}$$

$$= \frac{166\,030\ \text{J}}{156\ \text{W}}$$

$$= 1064\ \frac{\text{J}}{\text{J s}^{-1}} \quad (\text{since } 1\ \text{W} = 1\ \text{J s}^{-1})$$

$$= 1.1 \times 10^3\ \text{s to two significant figures}$$

This is approximately 18 minutes.

[Most of the values were given to two significant figures so the answer should also be given to two significant figures.]

3　Check that your answer makes sense

The calculation is complicated, so a little difficult to repeat with approximate values. However, from general knowledge, the answer seems reasonable (although this is not a recommended method for heating water!).

The units work out to be seconds, as expected for units of time.

This is likely to be an underestimate of the time taken because, in practice, not all of the electrical energy is converted into internal energy of the water (e.g. some is converted into the internal energy of the cup and its surroundings). So to supply the required amount of energy, the heater will need to operate for longer.

Activity 8.1

(a) 0.7% of 1 kg of hydrogen is $\dfrac{0.7}{100} \times 1\,\text{kg} = 7 \times 10^{-3}\,\text{kg}$.

Using Einstein's equation, $E = mc^2$, to calculate how much energy this is equivalent to:

$$E = mc^2$$
$$= 7 \times 10^{-3}\,\text{kg} \times (3.0 \times 10^8\,\text{m s}^{-1})^2$$
$$= 6.3 \times 10^{14}\,\text{kg m}^2\,\text{s}^{-2}$$
$$= 6 \times 10^{14}\,\text{J to one significant figure}$$

(b) The Sun's power is 4×10^{26} W, which is 4×10^{26} J of energy released each second.

From (a), you know that 6.3×10^{14} J is released from 1 kg hydrogen [note that the final rounded value is not used here, to avoid rounding errors – see Activity 4.2].

Thus 1 J is released from $\dfrac{1}{6.3 \times 10^{14}}$ kg and 4×10^{26} J is released from $\dfrac{4 \times 10^{26}}{6.3 \times 10^{14}}$ kg .

This is 6.3×10^{11} kg or 6×10^{11} kg to one significant figure. Thus 6×10^{11} kg of hydrogen is converted into helium each second.

(c) The time, t, required to convert all of the hydrogen into helium is given by:

$$t = \frac{\text{mass of hydrogen converted during lifetime of Sun}}{\text{mass of hydrogen converted per second}}$$

Now 75% of the initial mass of the Sun was hydrogen, which is:

$$\frac{75}{100} \times 2 \times 10^{30}\,\text{kg} = 1.5 \times 10^{30}\,\text{kg}$$

And 15% of this will be converted into helium during the Sun's lifetime, which is:

$$\frac{15}{100} \times 1.5 \times 10^{30}\,\text{kg} = 2.3 \times 10^{29}\,\text{kg}$$

So:

$$t = \frac{2.3 \times 10^{29} \text{ kg}}{6.3 \times 10^{11} \text{ kg s}^{-1}} = 3.7 \times 10^{17} \text{ s}$$

The number of seconds in a year is $365 \times 24 \times 60 \times 60 = 3.2 \times 10^7$, so the Sun's lifetime is approximately:

$$t = \frac{3.7 \times 10^{17}}{3.2 \times 10^7} \text{ years} = 1.2 \times 10^{10} \text{ years}$$

Thus, to one significant figure, the Sun's lifetime is 1×10^{10} years (i.e. 10 billion years).

Activity 9.1

Task 1

The upper graph in Figure 9.3 shows the displacement against distance at an instant of time, so it can be used to measure the wavelength. The lower graph shows the displacement against time at a fixed point in space, so it can be used to measure the period. The wavelength is $\lambda = 5.0$ cm and the period of the wave is $T = 2.0$ s. So the frequency of the wave is:

$$f = \frac{1}{T} = \frac{1}{2.0 \text{ s}} = 0.50 \text{ s}^{-1} = 0.50 \text{ Hz}$$

Therefore, the speed of propagation of the wave is
$v = f\lambda = 0.50 \text{ Hz} \times 5.0 \text{ cm} = 2.5 \text{ cm s}^{-1}$.

Task 2

(a) Table 9.4 shows some typical results which should be similar to those you have measured.

Table 9.4 Completed version of Table 9.1.

Order, n	Distance, s_n/mm
1	37
2	74
3	112
4	152
5	195
6	241

(b) Looking at the results in Table 9.4, you can see that as the order is doubled (say from $n = 1$ to $n = 2$, or from $n = 3$ to $n = 6$) so the distance of the spot from the centre of the pattern also approximately doubles. Similarly, the third order of the diffraction pattern is about three times further from the centre than the first order of the diffraction pattern, and so on. The results show that the distance s_n is roughly proportional to the order n of the diffraction pattern. Note, however, that the proportionality becomes increasingly approximate as s_n becomes large.

Task 3

(a) Table 9.5 shows some typical results which should be similar to your measured values.

(b) Looking at the results in Table 9.5, you can see that as d is reduced by a factor of three, from $d = 10.0$ µm to $d = 3.3$ µm, so the distance of the first order spot from the centre of the diffraction pattern *increases* roughly by a factor of three. Similarly, as d is halved from $d = 3.3$ µm to $d = 1.7$ µm, so s_n is approximately doubled. The results indicate that the distance, s_n, is roughly proportional to $\frac{1}{d}$.

Alternatively, you could say that, roughly speaking, s_n is inversely proportional to d.

Table 9.5 Completed version of Table 9.2.

Line spacing, d/µm	Distance, s_1/mm
10.0	37
3.3	112
1.7	243

Activity 9.2

Task I

A completed set of data is shown in Table 9.6.

Table 9.6 Completed version of Table 9.3.

Order, n	θ_n/degrees	sin θ_n
0	0.0	0.000
1	3.5	0.061
2	7.5	0.131
3	11.0	0.191
4	15.0	0.259
5	18.5	0.317
6	22.5	0.383

Tasks 2 and 3

A graph of the data is shown in Figure 9.11. To make maximum use of the paper, a convenient vertical scale is one 1 cm division for every change of 0.05 in $\sin \theta_n$, and a convenient horizontal scale is two 1 cm divisions for every change of 1 in n. Note that the best-fit straight line does not pass through all the points; one is above the line and one below it.

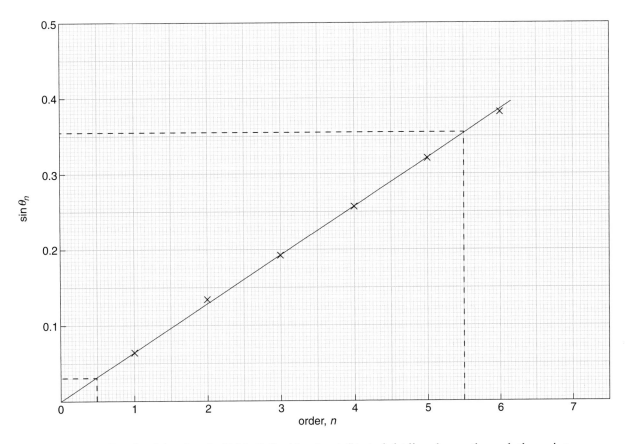

Figure 9.11 Graph of the data in Table 9.6 with a best-fit straight line drawn through the points.

Task 4

The gradient of the line shown in Figure 9.11 is given by:

$$\begin{aligned}
\text{gradient} &= \frac{\text{rise}}{\text{run}} \\
&= \frac{0.355 - 0.030}{5.5 - 0.5} \\
&= \frac{0.325}{5.0} \\
&= 0.065
\end{aligned}$$

Since neither $\sin \theta_n$ nor n have any units associated with them, the gradient has no unit either.

Equation 9.4 states that $\sin \theta_n = \left(\dfrac{\lambda}{d} \right) \times n$, so the gradient of a graph of $\sin \theta_n$ against n is equal to $\dfrac{\lambda}{d}$:

$$\text{gradient} = \frac{\lambda}{d}$$

so $\lambda = d \times \text{gradient}$

In this case, $d = 10.0 \ \mu\text{m} = 10.0 \times 10^{-6} \ \text{m} = 1.00 \times 10^{-5} \ \text{m}$

so $\lambda = 1.00 \times 10^{-5} \ \text{m} \times 0.065 = 6.5 \times 10^{-7} \ \text{m}$

The wavelengths of light are frequently quoted in nanometres (recall that $1 \ \text{nm} = 1 \times 10^{-9} \ \text{m}$ so, conversely, $1 \ \text{m} = 1 \times 10^{9} \ \text{nm}$) so

$6.5 \times 10^{-7} \ \text{m} = 6.5 \times 10^{-7} \times 10^{9} \ \text{nm} = 650 \ \text{nm}$.

Your answer should be within 50 nm of this value. In fact, the wavelength of the light from this laser is $6.36 \times 10^{-7} \ \text{m} = 636 \ \text{nm}$.

Activity 10.1

(a) If photoelectrons are emitted when a light is shone on a metal, increasing the intensity of the light will increase the number of photoelectrons emitted, but the range of energies of the photoelectrons will be unaffected.

If photoelectrons are not emitted when a light is shone on a metal, increasing the intensity of the light will have no effect whatsoever.

(b) If photoelectrons are emitted when a light is shone on a metal, increasing the frequency of the light will increase the maximum kinetic energy of the photoelectrons.

If photoelectrons are not emitted when a light is shone on a metal, increasing the frequency of the light will, for an appropriate metal, eventually result in the emission of photoelectrons.

(c) Changing the metal can alter the lower frequency limit for which photoelectrons are emitted. It can also alter the maximum kinetic energy of the photoelectrons.

Activity 11.1

Task 1

Figure 11.9a shows a photograph of the diffraction pattern produced by a tungsten filament light bulb in the arrangement shown in Figure 11.2. *Note*: if you have difficulty distinguishing colours, please refer to the labels on Figure 11.9b which should help you determine which colours are in each part of the pattern.

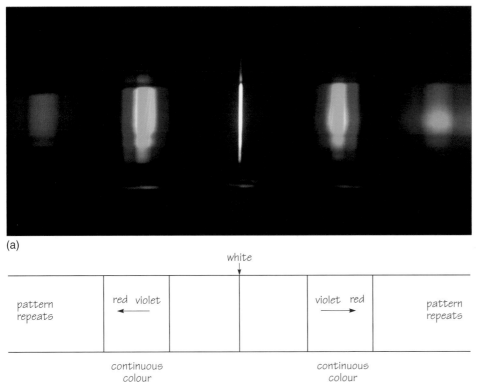

(a)

(b)

Figure 11.9 (a) Diffraction pattern from a tungsten filament light bulb. (b) Sketch of the diffraction pattern from a tungsten filament light bulb.

Your notes describing the diffraction pattern may include some of the following points.

- The same rainbow pattern of colours is repeated (at least) twice on either side of centre. The pattern becomes fainter in the outer regions.

- The pattern is essentially the same on left- and right-hand sides of the centre, but pattern to the left is a 'mirror image' of that to the right. (One side will probably appear somewhat fainter than the other.)

- Each spectrum (i.e. each order) has violet nearest to the centre, and passes through blue, green, yellow, orange and red in sequence away from the centre.

- The spread (i.e. width) of the spectrum is greater in second order than in the first order.

- The zero order diffraction pattern (at the position of the slit in the card) appears as a line of white light.

Task 2

Figure 11.10a shows a photograph of the diffraction pattern produced by an energy-saving light bulb in the arrangement shown in Figure 11.2. *Note*: as in Task 1, if you have difficulty distinguishing colours, please refer to the labels on Figure 11.10b which should help you determine which colours are in each part of the pattern.

Figure 11.10 (a) Diffraction pattern from an energy-saving light bulb. (b) Sketch of the diffraction pattern from an energy-saving light bulb.

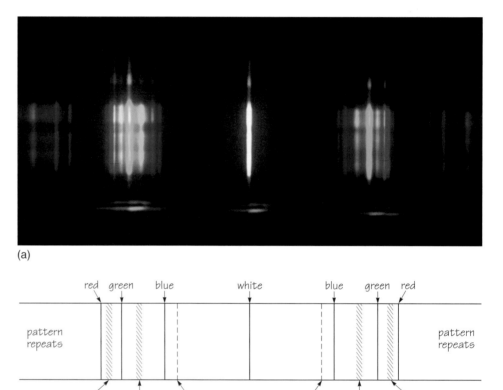

(a)

(b)

Your notes describing the pattern may include some of the following points.

• More orders of the diffraction pattern are clearly visible than with the tungsten filament bulb. Same pattern of coloured lines is repeated (at least) three times on either side of the centre, i.e. three orders are visible.

• As with the previous bulb, the pattern is essentially the same to left and right of the centre. Pattern on the left is a 'mirror image' of that on the right. (As with the first bulb, the pattern on one side will probably be fainter than the other.)

• Within each order, several bright, coloured lines are visible. Closest to the centre of the pattern each order has a faint, violet line (this is only just visible – sensitivity to violet decreases with age, so don't worry if you can't see it!) Next is a sharp, bright, deep blue line, then a rather broad and diffuse turquoise line, and then a bright green line. (The green line can actually be distinguished as two lines very close together if the slit is narrow enough.) Further out still is a series of fainter (blurred) orange lines followed by a sharp, bright red line. Beyond the bright red line are several fainter red lines (which blur together as they fade away).

- The spread of the spectrum increases progressively in moving from the first order to the second and third orders. (In fact, the red line of the second order of the pattern is very close to the blue line from the third order. If you can just glimpse the fourth order series of lines at the extremities of vision, you will note that the orange lines of the third order overlap the blue line from the fourth order.)

- The zero order of the diffraction pattern (at the position of the slit in the card) appears as a line of white light.

Tasks 3 and 4

Some typical results are listed in Table 11.3. Note that these angles should be the same whether measured in the left or right orders of the diffraction pattern. Values for the angles in the fourth order are also shown, in case you were able to measure any lines in this order. The values that you measured are probably within one or two degrees of those given in Table 11.3.

Table 11.3 Completed version of Table 11.1.

Order, n	θ_n/degrees	Uncertainty in θ_n/degrees	$\sin \theta_n$	Uncertainty in $\sin \theta_n$
blue spectral line				
1	7.5	±1.0	0.13	±0.02
2	15.0	±1.0	0.26	±0.02
3	23.0	±1.0	0.39	±0.02
4	31.5	±1.0	0.52	±0.02
green spectral line				
1	9.5	±1.0	0.17	±0.02
2	19.0	±1.0	0.33	±0.02
3	29.5	±1.0	0.49	±0.02
4	41.0	±1.0	0.66	±0.02
red spectral line				
1	11.0	±1.0	0.19	±0.02
2	22.0	±1.0	0.37	±0.02
3	34.0	±1.0	0.56	±0.02
4	49.0	±1.0	0.75	±0.02

Tasks 5 and 6

Graphs illustrating the data in Table 11.3 are shown in Figure 11.11. A point corresponding to $n = 0$ has been included in each case. Your graphs should be similar to these.

The graphs also show best-fit straight lines in each case. Note how each of the straight lines passes through a portion of each error bar, including that at $n = 0$, and that there are roughly as many points on one side of the line as on the other.

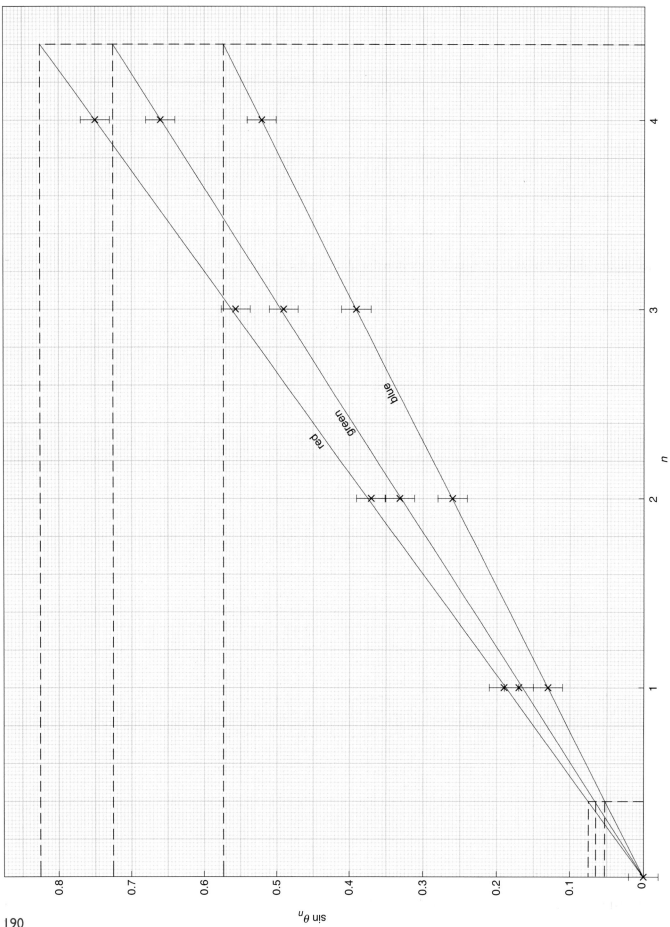

Task 7

The gradients of each of the three graphs in Figure 11.11 are calculated as the 'rise' in value up the vertical axis divided by the 'run' in value along the horizontal axis. The results are as follows.

blue line: gradient $= \dfrac{0.573 - 0.053}{4.40 - 0.40} = \dfrac{0.520}{4.00} = 0.130$

green line: gradient $= \dfrac{0.725 - 0.065}{4.40 - 0.40} = \dfrac{0.660}{4.00} = 0.165$

red line: gradient $= \dfrac{0.825 - 0.075}{4.40 - 0.40} = \dfrac{0.750}{4.00} = 0.188$

Since neither $\sin \theta_n$ nor n have any units associated with them, the gradient has no unit either.

The gradients of your graphs will probably be within about 0.01 or so of the numbers here. In each case, the gradient is equal to the wavelength of the spectral line divided by the line spacing of the grating. Hence the wavelengths of the three spectral lines are as follows.

blue line:

$\lambda = d \times \text{gradient} = (3.33 \times 10^{-6} \text{ m}) \times 0.130 = 4.33 \times 10^{-7} \text{ m} = 433 \text{ nm}$

green line:

$\lambda = d \times \text{gradient} = (3.33 \times 10^{-6} \text{ m}) \times 0.165 = 5.49 \times 10^{-7} \text{ m} = 549 \text{ nm}$

red line:

$\lambda = d \times \text{gradient} = (3.33 \times 10^{-6} \text{ m}) \times 0.188 = 6.26 \times 10^{-7} \text{ m} = 626 \text{ nm}$

Clearly, you could draw a range of lines through each set of points, each of which passed through most of the error bars, but each of which produced a slightly different value for the gradient. Each of these gradients in turn would result in a slightly different value for the wavelength of the spectral line in question. For instance, for the blue spectral line, gradients in the range from about 0.125 to 0.140 are all feasible with the data shown in Figure 11.11. This in turn leads to wavelength values between about 415 nm and 465 nm – that is, from about 20 nm below to about 30 nm above the 'best' value calculated above. (Given more time, you could determine upper and lower limits to the gradients for each of your data sets, and so calculate upper and lower limits for the individual wavelengths. However, you are *not* expected to do this here.) Bearing in mind the limitations discussed above, it would be unwise to quote the calculated wavelengths to more than two significant figures, since this would imply that there is confidence in the value to an accuracy of a few nanometres. Instead, quoting the wavelengths to only two significant figures implies that the wavelengths are accurate to a few tens of nanometres.

Figure 11.11   Graph (opposite page) showing $\sin \theta_n$ against n for the blue, green and red spectral lines, using the data listed in Table 11.3. Note how the best-fit lines here suggest experimental uncertainties may have been overestimated (see Fig 11.6 (a)).

The wavelengths can therefore be expressed as follows:

$$\lambda_{blue} = 4.3 \times 10^{-7} \text{ m} = 430 \text{ nm to two significant figures}$$
$$\lambda_{green} = 5.5 \times 10^{-7} \text{ m} = 550 \text{ nm to two significant figures}$$
$$\lambda_{red} = 6.3 \times 10^{-7} \text{ m} = 630 \text{ nm to two significant figures}$$

Task 8

Rearranging Equation 9.2 to make f the subject gives $f = \dfrac{c}{\lambda}$. So, for the three lines whose wavelengths were measured in Task 7, the frequencies are as follows:

blue line: $f = \dfrac{3.00 \times 10^8 \text{ m s}^{-1}}{4.33 \times 10^{-7} \text{ m}} = 6.93 \times 10^{14} \text{ Hz}$

green line: $f = \dfrac{3.00 \times 10^8 \text{ m s}^{-1}}{5.49 \times 10^{-7} \text{ m}} = 5.46 \times 10^{14} \text{ Hz}$

red line: $f = \dfrac{3.00 \times 10^8 \text{ m s}^{-1}}{6.26 \times 10^{-7} \text{ m}} = 4.79 \times 10^{14} \text{ Hz}$

Since the calculated wavelengths are only accurate to a few tens of nanometres (and quoted to two significant figures), the frequencies too should only be quoted to a similar level of accuracy, as 6.9×10^{14} Hz, 5.5×10^{14} Hz and 4.8×10^{14} Hz, respectively.

Task 9

Equation 10.1 states that the photon energy corresponding to a particular frequency of light is given by $E_{ph} = hf$ where h is the Planck constant and has a value of 4.14×10^{-15} eV Hz^{-1}. So, for the three spectral lines whose frequencies were calculated in Task 8, the corresponding photon energies are as follows:

blue line: $E_{ph} = (4.14 \times 10^{-15} \text{ eV Hz}^{-1}) \times (6.93 \times 10^{14} \text{ Hz}) = 2.9 \text{ eV}$

green line: $E_{ph} = (4.14 \times 10^{-15} \text{ eV Hz}^{-1}) \times (5.46 \times 10^{14} \text{ Hz}) = 2.3 \text{ eV}$

red line: $E_{ph} = (4.14 \times 10^{-15} \text{ eV Hz}^{-1}) \times (4.79 \times 10^{14} \text{ Hz}) = 2.0 \text{ eV}$

As above, a final quoted accuracy for the photon energies of two significant figures reflects the uncertainties in the procedure you have carried out.

Activity 12.1

Are there skills listed in Table 12.1 where you still feel lacking in confidence? If so, start by thinking about whether your self-appraisal is reasonable – are you *really* struggling with the skills? How well did you get on with the relevant assessment questions? You may find the comments from your tutor, when you receive them, useful in judging how well you really did.

Table 12.2 gives some suggestions about what to do in areas where you are genuinely struggling. Frequently, the advice starts by suggesting that you look back to the part of the course where the skill was first taught. You may find it easier to understand on reading for a second time, especially now that you have moved on in your reading of the course.

For the mathematical and problem-solving skills, try all the questions that you can find. Mathematical skills are best learned by practice. Practice can help with the practical skills too. There is another experiment in Book 5 (Activity 2.1) and many of the skills can be practised in other ways; for example, you can practise observational skills when watching a video sequence.

If you are still struggling, why not post a message on your tutor group forum? A fellow student may have experienced similar difficulties, and have found a way through. If your fellow students are struggling too, you will probably feel better after talking to people with the same difficulty.

Don't forget to talk to your tutor who is there to help you and will be pleased to hear from you. In the case of practical difficulties (e.g. if you were unable to complete an experiment because of problems with your dexterity or sight), there are specific things they can do to help.

Table 12.2 Suggestions for improving the skills considered in Table 12.1.

Skill requiring further practice	What to do
Using symbols for quantities and units	Look back to Book 2, Section 11.2.1. You may also find it helpful to check that your personal glossary of symbols and equations (Book 3, Activity 4.1) is up to date and especially that you have noted the meanings of the terms as you used them.
Rearranging equations	See Section 3.3 of this book, and use every opportunity available to you to practise. You may also find it helpful to watch the video sequence *Rearranging Equations* (Activity 3.2) again.
Solving problems	See Activities 4.2 and 5.1. Questions 4.6 and 5.4 are specifically designed to help you develop problem-solving skills; however, these skills may be practised in numerous other questions, both mathematical and otherwise. Remember to think carefully about what you are trying to find and to check that your answer is reasonable.
Working out the units	You may find it helpful to watch the video sequence *Working out the Units* (Activity 4.2) again.
Significant figures	Significant figures were introduced in Book 1, Section 3.1.4. Useful guidance is also given in Book 3, Activity 4.2.
Combining equations	See Section 5.6 of this book.
Proportionality	You were introduced to direct proportionality in Section 4.1.2 and then you learned how this relates to straight-line graphs in Section 7.5.1. Inverse proportionality was introduced in Activity 9.1.
Plotting graphs	This course assumes that you have plotted graphs before but this skill was revised in Book 2, Activity 7.1. If you find it difficult to plot graphs by hand, perhaps because of problems with your dexterity or sight, you should talk to your tutor.
Drawing best-fit straight lines	See Book 2, Box 6.1. Revised in Book 2, Activity 7.1.
Calculating the gradient of a straight-line graph	See Book 2, Box 6.1.
Relating the gradient of a graph to the equation of a straight line	Make sure that you understand Section 7.5.1 (Proportionality and straight-line graphs) then re-read Section 7.5.2 (The equation of a straight line).
Finding the sine of an angle	See Section 9.2.2, and make sure that you can use your calculator to find the sine of an angle.

Following the instructions for practical work	If you find it difficult to understand instructions given in the text it might be worth thinking about your study skills more generally. For example, are you following the advice given on 'active reading' in Book 1, Section 1.2.1? Try reading a section of text and then closing the book and summarising what it said in your own words. Can you remember the important points of what you have read? Understanding written text is very important throughout your study of S104, not just when you are doing practical work.
Setting up experiments	If you couldn't set up the experiment in Activity 11.1, is there a friend or family member who could help you? This experiment is quite fiddly and, if you are still having difficulty, you should talk to your tutor.
Observing experimental results	Observational skills are developed throughout S104 both in practical work and in many of the video sequences and other computer-based activities. Observational skills are very important in the study of science.
Taking measurements	If you find it difficult to take measurements because of problems with your dexterity or sight, you should talk to your tutor. Is there a friend, family member or fellow student who could help you? Provided you are telling this person what readings to take and you are doing the calculations, this is not cheating.
Estimating uncertainties	Read the comments just before Task 3 in Activity 11.1, and look again at Book 1, Section 3.1.2.
Keeping a record of an experiment	See the advice given in the introduction to Activity 11.1. Remember to note everything you might need to know in order to tell someone else how you did the experiment and write down all your results. It is also important to keep your notes somewhere safe, perhaps in a notebook or in your study folder.
Calculating the results of an experiment	In exactly the same way as when answering questions and solving problems, remember to take your time and to write down all your working. You may find the advice in Activity 4.2 helpful.
Writing a report on experimental work	See Activity 6.2. If you are still not clear what to include in a report on practical work you should talk to your tutor. The general rule is that you should include enough information to enable a fellow-student to repeat the experiment on the strength of your report alone.

Acknowledgements

The S104 Course Team gratefully acknowledges the contributions of the S103 *Discovering science* course team and of its predecessors.

Grateful acknowledgement is made to the following sources for permission to reproduce material in this book.

Figures

Cover: Eric Heller/Science Photo Library;

Figure 1.1: Pekka Parviainen/Science Photo Library;

Figure 2.4: © Kumar Sriskandan/Alamy; Figure 2.5a: Martin Bond/Science Photo Library; Figure 2.5b: Denis Doyle/Getty Images;

Figure 4.4: AFP/Getty Images;

Figure 5.7: © Tony Waltham/Robert Harding World Imagery/Corbis; Figure 5.9: Lindsay Polly Crisp; Figure 5.11: © Stefan Matzke/NewSport/Corbis;

Figure 7.7: Roger Courthold;

Figure 8.2a: © Geogphotos/Alamy; Figure 8.3b: NASA Jet Propulsion Laboratory (NASA-JPL); Figure 8.3c: © Jenny Matthews/Alamy; Figure 8.4a: SOHO (ESA & NASA); Figure 8.4b: Martin Bond/Science Photo Library; Figure 8.5b: Gordon Garradd/Science Photo Library; Figure 8.17b: Ted Kinsman/Science Photo Library; Figure 8.17c: Gustoimages/Science Photo Library;

Figure 9.1: Peter Kaminski/Flickr Photo Sharing;

Figures 11.2, 11.3a, 11.3b, 11.9a and 11.10a: Sally Jordan; Figure 11.7: AIP Emilio Segre Visual Archives, *Physics Today* Collection; Figure 11.8a: Courtesy of Naomi Williams and Goodfellow;

Every effort has been made to contact copyright holders. If any have been inadvertently overlooked the publishers will be pleased to make the necessary arrangements at the first opportunity.

Index

Entries and page numbers in **bold type** refer to key words that are printed in **bold** in the text and that are defined in the Glossary. Where the page number is given in *italics*, the index information is carried mainly or wholly in an illustration, table or box.